HOUSING ADAPTATIONS FOR
DISABLED PEOPLE

Housing Adaptations for Disabled People

Terence Lockhart AIAS

Published for the
DISABLED LIVING FOUNDATION by
THE ARCHITECTURAL PRESS: London

First published in 1981 by The Architectural Press Ltd:
London

ISBN: 0 85139 331 4 paper

Printed in Great Britain by Mackays of Chatham Ltd

Contents

Acknowledgements

I am greatly indebted to Lady Hamilton, the Chairman of the Disabled Living Foundation, and to her staff for their enthusiasm and support in the making of this publication. I would also like to express my considerable appreciation to all members of the steering group set up by the Foundation to advise me on the accuracy and content of the book. Their professional guidance and expertise were invaluable, as were the most generous grants from British Gas and Marks and Spencer Ltd., without which the book would not have been possible.

My gratitude is also due to the very many individual people, manufacturers and organisations who provided photographs, illustrations, case studies and written contributions, or who commented on particular sections; and to the disabled people and their families who must remain anonymous but who freely gave detailed and helpful information for some of the case studies. It is not possible to list everyone who contributed to making this a more informative book, but I would like to thank particularly:

Association of District Councils
Association of Environmental Health Officers
Centre on Environment for the Handicapped
Mrs J. Cobbett
Mrs E. Grove, FBAOT
Mrs J. Higgins, MBAOT SROT
Mrs E. Lockhart, ACII
London Borough of Havering (Architects' Division)
London Borough of Wandsworth (Department of Social Services and Department of Development)
Mrs S. Macdonald, MBAOT SROT
Mr L. Mason

Mr D. A. G. Morris
Dr J. A. Muir Gray, MB ChB (Glasgow) DPH
Mr J. H. Penton, BA AADipl RIBA MSIAB ACIArb
Mr L. Pescodd
Surrey County Council
Miss C. M. Tarling, MBAOT
Tewkesbury Borough Council (Environmental Health Department)
Mr H. Titcombe, MBAOT SROT

Terry Lockhart
Brentwood 1981

Members of the Steering Group

Lady Hamilton, CBE MA   Chairman, Disabled Living Foundation

Mr W. G. Apps, Dip Arch (Hons) FRIBA   Assistant County Architect, Essex County Council

Mrs B. J. Banham, CBE JP BSc DipSocSt.   Director, Disabled Living Foundation

Mrs H. Binks, MCSP   Welfare Officer, British Rheumatism and Arthritis Association

Mrs S. Cooper, BSc MIH CertEd   Representative, the Institute of Housing

Miss H. J. Connell, SRN SCM HVCert (until April 26, 1979)   Welfare Secretary, The Multiple Sclerosis Society

Mr T. J. Davies (from April 26, 1979)   Welfare Secretary, The Multiple Sclerosis Society

Mr E. S. Higgins, OBE   Trustee, Disabled Living Foundation
Former Director of Social Services, London Borough of Wandsworth
Chairman, Directors of Social Services Committee, London Boroughs Association

Mrs E. Lloyd, SROT   Senior Occupational Therapist, Harrow Social Services

Mrs S. Lomas, MBAOT   Assistant Director and Head of Information Service, Disabled Living Foundation

Mr H. D. Macfarlane   Liaison Officer, Association for Spina Bifida and Hydrocephalus

Mr D. J. Sandford, MIH   Representative, Association of District Councils

Foreword

In the early spring of 1977, Mr Terry Lockhart, a building surveyor working on adaptations to dwellings for disabled people, consulted Mrs Sarah Lomas, Head of the Disabled Living Foundation's Information Service for the Disabled, about a book he was compiling on adaptations to dwellings for physically handicapped people. The Disabled Living Foundation's Trustees were particularly interested to learn of this since, for many years, they had been disquieted by the difficulties encountered in getting satisfactory adaptations to the houses and flats of disabled people which might be much needed to improve the quality of life, or make life more livable for both the disabled person and his family.

It had seemed to the Trustees that these difficulties had often arisen because the person who advised the adaptations could be an occupational therapist or social worker who knew a great deal about disabled people and their needs, but very little about building; whereas the work decided on would then be carried out by architects or surveyors and builders who knew a great deal about building but usually very little about disabled people. Hence, all too often, disabled people and their families got the worst of both worlds. A distressing and usual aspect of such adaptations was the long delays due to the complication of the legal situation and the arrangements for obtaining finance for the work, which needed the approval of committees meeting infrequently. Apart from short publications dealing with specialised aspects, there seemed to be little reference available for those concerned, whether the adviser or the builder, or the disabled person. A textbook seemed urgently needed to develop all the circumstances – legislation for both major and minor adaptation, grants, design and building information – which could be useful not only to disabled people but to all disciplines involved, whether concerned with disabled people or with building.

The Trustees welcomed Mr Lockhart's approach and it was agreed that he should undertake his work under the auspices of the Disabled Living Foundation. A multi-disciplinary Advisory Panel was enrolled to consider the individual chapters and to advise generally on content. Mr Lockhart, with their help, began the arduous task of writing and rewriting drafts on a truly complicated and difficult subject. *Housing Adaptations for Disabled People* is the result of much time most generously given by members of the Advisory Panel and many hours of work on the part of the author. The Disabled Living Foundation's Trustees are deeply grateful to the members of the Advisory Panel and Mr Lockhart. They also thank the County Architect and the Director of Social Services to Surrey County Council for their permission to refer to case material relating to particular projects.

Housing Adaptations for Disabled People is intended to meet the need for practical information to fill the gaps in knowledge and to provide a book of reference for all concerned. It will be noted that the book includes four long case studies. These show how very complicated the whole apparently simple matter of adapting a dwelling can be from every point of view. Those advising the alterations have to consider all the circumstances of the disabled person and his family.

The whole process can involve enormous delays which, to a disabled person, may seem needlessly uncaring, since the distress of his predicament and the extent of his personal hardship may appear not to have been appreciated. If there is any point which emerges from all others in this book, it is that everyone concerned should appreciate the need for greater urgency in matters concerning alterations to dwellings for disabled people.

Mr Lockhart's book is designed to be read by individual disabled people and their families, and the occupational therapists, social workers, architects, surveyors and builders who advise them on the often vital subject of alterations to the home to make it more useful to them and to minimise the disadvantages which their disability has caused. It is hoped that those social groups who would not, necessarily, expect to become clients of the social services department or to need a grant to enable alterations to be done, will also find the book helpful; and that such people may be made more aware that local-authority staffs are empowered to offer them helpful and useful advice, even if these staffs never become involved in either the finance or the arrangement of the building work. Additionally, it is hoped that the book will be helpful to those teaching professional qualifications of various kinds, to staffs of voluntary bodies and to manufacturers of the items described.

Although *Housing Adaptations for Disabled People* describes the circumstances surrounding adaptations in this country, and sections of it are directly applicable only to England and Wales (because of the legislation and finance arrangements involved), much of it is of more general application. Much of the advice on adaptations and many of the building points will have international relevance where there is a similar way of life, and Appendix D lists information sources in 17 countries which may be contacted for more specific local data. It is therefore hoped that this book, which we believe to be unique as a textbook, will be widely useful internationally.

The finance for compiling the manuscript came jointly from British Gas and Marks and Spencers Limited, who presented the Disabled Living Foundation with a generous cheque, the result of a very successful series of cookery demonstrations which they had jointly undertaken. We are deeply grateful to Lord Sieff and the Board of Marks and Spencers, and to Sir Denis Rooke and the Board of British Gas Corporation, for their most important help. We hope that they will be pleased with the book and that it may also, at some time, be helpful to the disabled members of their staff and their families.

Like all first efforts in any field, no doubt, there are omissions and some parts might be improved, although all concerned have done their best. Both the author and the Disabled Living Foundation's Trustees would be very glad to have any comment or feedback, in order to improve the second edition and make it more useful.

W. M. Hamilton

Introduction

The problems of everyday living which face disabled people are seldom appreciated by those who are able-bodied, until they are personally confronted with them. The causes of disability are many. A child may be born disabled, or a fit and healthy adult may have an accident or contract a disease, as a result of which he may have to spend the rest of his life on crutches or in a wheelchair. The pace of his life may be drastically reduced and he will probably be faced with practical difficulties in moving about, both inside and outside the home. Limited by his physical disability, the disabled person must find new ways of doing things. To be independent is the predominant motive of most disabled people and, to achieve that ambition, they will need not only a great deal of personal determination but all the help they can get from special aids and any adaptations that can be made to their homes to meet their particular needs.

A person may become disabled, or his condition deteriorate, after he has settled in a particular house or locality and, since he will be dependent on close relatives or good neighbours for comfort and support, the adaptation of an existing house may be preferable to rehousing him in a purpose-built unit in an area where he knows no one. Such a building may be more practical but, if the disabled person is unhappy because he has been uprooted and his social links severed, the disadvantages of moving may well outweigh the advantages.

Although the purpose of an adaptation is to provide the facilities required to meet the needs of a particular disabled person, it is seldom necessary to alter every feature in the home. The alterations will be mainly confined to commonly used rooms, where inconvenience or obstruction occurs. For example, if a ground floor self-contained extension is proposed, the

1

doorways on the first floor may not need to be widened.

The degree of handicap will dictate the type of adaptation necessary, but it is important that it should not be carried out in isolation; the other able-bodied members of the household should also be considered before any adaptation is made. Structural alterations and modifications for wheelchair users are obviously more drastic and costly than those for ambulant disabled people. More emphasis is, therefore, given in this book to alterations intended to meet the needs of wheelchair users.

The book is intended to be a useful guide for all those personally involved, professionally or otherwise, in this important subject. It outlines, in simple terms, some of the common everyday problems which occur and tries to explain the relevant legislation and administrative procedures followed by local authorities in Great Britain. It seeks to fill the gap that exists between the 'sociological' approach to disability and the mass of information about aids and equipment. Deliberate emphasis is placed on the practical problems with which the occupational therapist will be faced, of fitting the hardware and altering the structure, but some information is also given about the various forms of handicap and their assessment, which will be of benefit to the architect. The four case studies of adaptations in Appendix A are intended to give an overall picture of the types of problem which may be encountered and the ways in which they can be overcome, always bearing in mind the individual needs of the disabled person.

It is important to emphasise from the outset that the definitions of 'disabled' and 'handicap' used throughout this book are not synonymous. A disability is an impairment which can be diagnosed by a doctor, whereas a handicap is an inconvenience or difficulty created by that impairment, to the detriment of the disabled person. This book offers guidance on how the adaptation of a disabled person's home can alleviate his handicap and generally make his life easier, safer and more comfortable.

1 Procedure and legislation

1.1 General approach

Wide powers are available in the UK to both housing and social-service authorities to undertake or provide assistance in the adaptation of housing for disabled people. Section 2 of the UK Chronically Sick and Disabled Persons Act 1970 provides that social-service authorities, in exercising their powers under section 29 of the National Assistance Act 1948 to provide for the welfare of disabled people, should make arrangements for adaptations to the homes of a disabled person where these are needed in the interests of greater safety, comfort or convenience.

Section 3 of the Act states explicitly that housing authorities should take into account the special needs of disabled people in discharging their duty under section 91 of the Housing Act 1957 to consider the housing conditions and needs of their district for further housing accommodation. Their powers extend to adaptation of existing accommodation.

Since the overlap in the powers of UK housing and social-service authorities has resulted in some uncertainty about where the responsibility should lie in particular cases, a Joint Circular was prepared, entitled *Adaptations of housing for people who are physically-handicapped.* * Broadly speaking, the Joint Circular proposes that responsibility for identifying, assessing and advising on the housing needs for individual disabled people – including the need for adaptations to their homes – should remain with social services departments, in collaboration with health authorities. Housing authorities should be responsible for work involving structural alterations to houses owned or managed by

* Department of the Environment, Department of Health and Social Security and the Welsh Office, Circular 59/78.

3

them, whereas social-services departments should deal with non-structural modifications and the provision of aids and equipment.

In the UK private sector, housing authorities do not have comprehensive powers to adapt owner-occupied or privately rented housing. Social-service authorities will, therefore, as a result of their duty under section 2 of the 1970 Act, continue to be the primary source of help with such adaptations. However, housing authorities have a broad discretion to assist in the private sector by means of improvement grants under section 56 of the Housing Act 1974. These grants are available to disabled people on a wider basis than to others, and the Joint Circular asks housing authorities to take advantage of these powers to give grants to those who need them.

It is essential that the initial contact should be between the disabled person and his local social-services department, since it is that department which has the responsibility for identifying, assessing and advising on housing needs and adaptations. However, the amount of financial aid given, and the administrative procedures to be followed (discussed later), vary enormously from one locality to another.

In the first instance, the difficulties encountered by physically disabled people living at home may be brought to the attention of the social-service authorities by:

i the disabled person himself or his family or friends
ii social-services staff including social workers
iii health-services workers eg hospital consultant, occupational therapist, physiotherapist, family doctor, health visitor, community nurse
iv housing-authority staff eg rent collectors, estate officers
v social-security officer
vi voluntary agencies.

Within the local authority, adaptations are usually assessed, and organised, by occupational therapists (usually abbreviated to OT), although other social-services staff may perform this duty if OTs are not employed. In some areas, OTs may also be known as 'rehabilitation officers' or 'disabled living advisers', or by some other similar title. However, for the sake of brevity, the term 'OT' is used throughout this book. Similarly, when a disabled person is referred to, 'he' automatically includes 'she'.

In this context, the OT's main purpose is to make functional assessments of people who are physically disabled or mentally handicapped and help with their emotional problems and psychological welfare, in co-operation with the social worker, if necessary. Their duties entail looking after the *overall* requirements of their client and teaching or advising him on the different methods of coping with his handicap and helping him to plan any necessary adaptations.

The preliminary discussion with the disabled person and the assessment by the social-services department are of prime importance, because extra time spent at this stage will be of great value in the long term. It is necessary for the OT to ascertain the psychological effect of the disability, the suitability of the various personal aids or equipment and the anxiety involved in proceeding with the adaptation – particularly where major building work is entailed. In some circumstances, if the disabled person is elderly or frail, for instance, the upheaval or inconvenience may not be worthwhile and the social services department may have to suggest that a particular proposal may be too distressing. Each application must be decided on its merits, as there is no stock solution which can be universally applied.

The design of structural adaptations is normally carried out by an architect but, equally, it may be undertaken by a surveyor or any technical person with the requisite specialised knowledge. For the sake of brevity, however, the term 'architect' is used in this book. Minor adaptations are generally regarded as work of a non-structural nature and the architect need not always be involved (see also Chapter 2 Minor adaptations).

Implementing structural adaptations is very much a multi-professional task and, if the result is to be successful, the architect and OT must work as a team with the disabled person and his family. Where possible, joint site visits should be made, so that the disabled person or householder and his family can be fully involved and make helpful suggestions on site to the architect and OT. The client, who will obviously be familiar with his own disability and his own house, can save the architect many hours of work over the drawing board; on the other hand, the architect will be in a position to spot defects or contraventions of current building legislation about which the layman would not be aware. If grant aid is to be sought, the Environmental Health or Housing Officer should be invited to visit the site, in the initial stages, with all the parties involved, since the availability of financial help could influence the type of scheme proposed.

No matter how feasible an adaptation may appear to the architect or how suitable it may seem to the OT, no scheme can be entertained if the disabled person and his family object to it on principle. The outcome must be a joint decision. The proposal that a lift should be installed often causes problems. It would often be much easier and more practicable to install a lift than to build an extension to provide ground-floor accommodation to replace previously inaccessible first-floor accommodation (see Chapter 5 Lifts). However, a disabled person may refuse the offer of a lift because he is frightened of it, or because he feels that a lift in his only reception room would be unduly obtrusive and tend to act as a constant reminder of his disability.

The selection of a particular type of adaptation is not always obvious, since there may be two or three courses to consider in any given situation. The experience of the architect should be helpful, since he can provide cost comparisons or other relevant data. Similarly, the experienced OT should be able to assess the present needs and long-term effects upon the disabled person's welfare, mobility and independence.

Every successful adaptation must be tailor-made to suit the particular person and his home. Theoretical space requirements and dimensional data are available to guide those designing new buildings, but most adaptations involve working within existing physical constraints and some compromises are often necessary.

The design of an adaptation should take into account the decrease in functional ability that results from aging and from the possible progress of the disabling condition. In every case, the professional staff advising on adaptations should consult the disabled person's doctor to ensure that these adaptations make provision for any fluctuations in the underlying condition and the likely pattern of its progression. Building alterations suitable for a disabled person who uses a walking frame could become ineffective if that person became wheelchair-bound at a later date.

1.2 Contract particulars

Once the initial paperwork and financial arrangements have been agreed between the parties involved, the architect, whether employed privately or as an employee of the local authority, will visit the dwelling and take the relevant measurements. He should have a copy of the OT's report or brief, with its recommendations on the project, so that a sketch plan can be drawn up and submitted for approval.

A preliminary sketch plan is usually necessary only when a considerable amount of alteration or new building work is involved. If the disabled person or OT is not used to reading plans, the scheme should be clearly explained to them, as far as possible in non-technical language. The architect should point out any features which may not be immediately obvious or which have significantly influenced the design.

When the final detailed drawing has been scrutinised and accepted, the architect will apply to the local authority for Building Regulations approval on the prescribed forms. Large extensions will in the UK normally also need planning approval, but small or internal adaptations will usually constitute 'permitted development' and are exempt from planning requirements. However, it is obviously prudent to consult the local planning officer where any doubt exists. If the nature of the application is made known at, or before, the time of submission, the planning or building control officer may try to reduce delay by putting the application at the top of the list.

Depending on the nature of the contract, the architect will write a specification, a document which augments the information provided on the drawings and provides a fairer basis on which to obtain competitive tenders. Where the work is to be done by the disabled person's relatives, a lengthy specification is not necessary, but frequent site visits should be made to check that the drawing is adhered to and that all the work is being performed in a proper workman-like manner.

In most cases, the actual contract in the UK is between the local authority (but administered by the Borough or County Architect) and the building contractor. Some local authorities operate a reimbursement scheme whereby the disabled person employs his own builder and claims reimbursement on satisfactory completion of the work, subject to various conditions imposed by the authority.

Competitive tenders are usually sought from reputable local contractors on the council's approved list and, in most cases, the lowest estimate accepted. Alternatively, the architect may negotiate a price, on behalf of the local authority, with a single contractor. This avoids time-consuming tendering procedures, but it may be necessary to obtain a waiver of the local authorities' standing orders.

1.3 Building firms

The choice of contractor is important, not only because of cost, but because good relations and diplomacy are necessary to mitigate inconvenience and disturbance to the occupant. The contractor should make every effort to keep the noise level to a minimum, and keep the site as clean and tidy as possible. If it is necessary for the occupant to move out, the local housing department may provide him with temporary accommodation.

No fixed rules regulate the size of firm to be employed for these contracts. A small firm with a few employees may be overloaded with work and may not be able to start work on a large extension for many weeks. On the other hand, a large firm, unless it has a small works department, may regard a domestic adaptation as a mere 'stop gap' between large contracts and, consequently, programme the job to suit the firm rather than the occupant. (See also Case study no 1, p104.)

1.4 Delays

(See also Appendix A, Case studies of Adaptations, p104.)

All the necessary assessment and contractual procedures sometimes become unduly protracted, and the disabled client has to exercise tremendous patience. A delay which would result in inconvenience or nuisance to an able-bodied person could result in distress and great personal hardship to a disabled person. The delays in obtaining the necessary financial help and securing authorisation for the work to proceed are often a source of acrimony between the parties involved.

Some delays are inevitable owing to the complexity of local government procedures – the size of the various departments, their different methods of working and the number of people working under pressure on cases of equal urgency. In addition, some contractors are slower than others and private landlords are often difficult to contact.

It is understandably difficult for a disabled person, sitting at home, fully to appreciate the reasons for delay, and lack of information increases frustration. It is hoped, therefore, that this chapter provides some insight into the background work involved before any adaptation reaches fruition. Once building work has started, the occupant must resist the temptation to inferfere or obstruct progress. If he wants to vary the original design, he should consult the architect and not issue instructions to the builder himself (see Case study no 1, p104).

1.5 UK sources of finance

Financial assistance for adaptations is available from a number of sources, one being the Renovation Grant. Part VII of the Housing Act 1974 makes house renovation grants available for house improvement. The primary purpose of house renovation grants is to preserve the quality of the housing stock by improving and repairing older houses or converting large houses into smaller self-contained units. The grants are available to owner occupiers and private landlords. The environmental health officer will provide the necessary detailed and specialised advice.

The two types of renovation grant which may help disabled people are as follows.

Improvement grants

Section 56 (2) (a) of the Housing Act 1974 states that an improvement grant can be given for the improvement of a dwelling. In the case of a disabled person, this includes any works required for his welfare, accommodation or employment, if the existing dwelling is inadequate or unsuitable for those purposes. These grants are available at the discretion of the local authority to help owners to improve older houses to a good standard, or to provide dwellings by converting houses of an unsatisfactory size.

The local authority must be satisfied that, upon completion of the work, the dwelling will have all satisfactory sanitary facilities for the exclusive use of the occupants, will be in good repair, will be likely to have a useful life of 30 years, and will conform with the following 10-point standard:

i substantial freedom from damp
ii adequate natural lighting and ventilation in each habitable room

iii adequate and safe provision throughout for artificial lighting, and sufficient electric socket outlets for the safe and proper functioning of domestic applicances

iv adequate drainage facilities

v a stable structural condition

vi a satisfactory internal arrangement

vii adequate facilities for heating

viii satisfactory facilities for preparing and cooking food

ix proper provision for the storage of fuel (where necessary) and for the storage of refuse

x thermal insulation in the roofspace sufficient to give the relevant structure a U value of $0.4 \text{W/m}^2 \text{ °C}$.

The local authority can dispense with any of these requirements at their discretion.

Where improvement grants are offered by the local authority, they only cover a proportion of the money necessary to carry out the work. The cost of the remainder is met by the occupant, or, in the case of a disabled person, it may be met by the social services department. The maximum 'appropriate percentage' of an improvement grant payable by the local authority is usually 50 per cent (£2,500 maximum) but this can be increased to 60 per cent (£3,000 maximum) in a General Improvement Area, or 75 per cent (£3,750 maximum) in a Housing Action Area (as defined in the Housing Act 1974). In special cases of hardship, however, the housing authority has the power to meet up to 90 per cent of the cost of the work (£4,500 maximum).*

Subject to a maximum limitation, the grant may be increased to cover additional work, subsequently found to be necessary and which could not have been reasonably foreseen when the application was made. If an intermediate grant or grant under previous legislation has already been paid for work done to the house, an improvement grant to bring the house up to a better standard will be available, though this will be adjusted to take account of the earlier grant.

Intermediate grants
Section 56 (2) (b) of the Housing Act 1974 states that an intermediate grant is available for:

---

* Information correct at time of going to press.

. . . work required for the improvement of a dwelling by provision of standard amenities which it lacks, or which in the case of a disabled person are inaccessible to that person by virtue of his disability.

An intermediate grant is available for dwellings in which a disabled person is, or will be, living, if the standard amenities are missing, or where the existing amenities are inacessible because of his disability. Intermediate grants are available from local authorities to help meet the cost of providing any missing standard amenities, as set out below:

Standard amenity to be provided	Maximum eligible expense at Sept 1980
i Fixed bath or shower	£250
ii Hot and cold water supply to i	£300
iii Wash-basin	£100
iv Hot and cold water supply to iii	£150
v Sink	£250
vi Hot and cold water supply to v	£200
vii Wc	£350
	Total £1,600

The grant can also assist in the cost of repair and replacement up to an additional maximum eligible expense limit of £2,000, provided the local authority is satisfied that these are necessary for the dwelling to attain the relevant standard. The maximum 'appropriate percentage' of an intermediate grant is again 50 per cent (up to a maximum of £1,800) but this can be increased to 60 per cent (£2,160 maximum) in General Improvement Areas or 75 per cent to 90 per cent in Housing Action Areas (£2,700 to £3,240 maximum).

An intermediate grant is available as a right, provided that the following conditions, as well as the basic requirements applicable to all grants, are fulfilled upon completion of the work:

i the standard amenities are available for the exclusive use of the occupants

ii the dwelling will be in a good state of repair (disregarding internal decoration) having regard to its age, character and location iii it will have, in the roofspace, sufficient thermal insulation to give the relevant structure a U value of $0.4W/m^2$ °C

iv it will, in all other aspects, be fit for human habitation

v it is likely to be available as a dwelling house for at least 15 years.

Subject to the above conditions, a local authority cannot refuse a valid application for an intermediate grant but the authority may, at its discretion, reduce any of the conditions.

Householders who are themselves disabled, or have disabled people living with them, may be entitled to an improvement or intermediate grant to help adapt their homes where existing accommodation is unsuitable. The provision that grants are only available for houses built after 3 October 1961 does not apply when the improvements are to a dwelling occupied by a disabled person.

Apart from the specific conditions already referred to, house-renovation grants are subject to the following general conditions:

i the dwelling must have a useful 'life', and comply with the required standard upon completion of the works. The local authority do, however, have a discretion to waive any of the standards

ii the applicant, who need not be disabled, must have correct title to the house concerned. He must own the freehold of the property or have a leasehold interest with at least five years unexpired

iii when the grant is approved in respect of owner-occupied property, the applicant will have to certify that he will use the dwelling as his only or main residence for a period of five years after the grant has been paid, or, if he is unable to do this, after the first year, let the property

iv when the grant is approved in respect of a rented property, the landlord will have to certify that the dwelling will be let, or available for letting, as a residence, and not as a holiday home or to members of his family, for a period of five years after the grant has been paid

v if the house is sold during the five-year period, the owner will have to repay the grant, plus compound interest, upon demand from the local authority, who may, at their discretion, demand a lesser amount or make no demand at all.

The feasibility of an adaptation does not always depend on the financial help available from the local authority. The person concerned may, himself, be able to afford to pay for the necessary work, although many people would welcome any assistance that is forthcoming. The social-services department can advise on the possible financial help available from official sources, in the form of grants, reinbursement schemes, maturity loans or interest-free loans. Many local authorities operate a means test to maximise the benefits of limited departmental budgets. Alternatively, or in addition, money can be allocated according to the priorities of individual needs. A person in hospital, and unable to be discharged until his home is structurally altered, might be given higher priority than another disabled person being looked after reasonably well at home, but not able to be fully independent.

Other sources of finance
In cases of special hardship, money is occasionally available from charitable sources to subsidise funds from statutory bodies. An approach to these is usually made, on behalf of the disabled person, by the social worker involved, and the Disabled Living Foundation can suggest possible channels of access. It is prudent to check that the charitable grant or loan will not decrease the social-services subvention.

Maturity loans are increasingly being made available by local authorities to elderly or disabled people on fixed or low incomes. Under this scheme, the council advances a sum of money (principal) to the occupant so that he may carry out adaptations or improvements to his home (see Case study no 4, p116). The advance is secured by a charge on the property and the occupant can choose from the following alternatives:

i he can enter into a covenant to repay the advance, over a period to be agreed (normally 5 to 10 years), by equal monthly instalments of principal and interest

ii he can make monthly repayments of interest only, leaving the principal outstanding. Under this method, the council would not, provided that repayments of interest were regularly maintained, recall the principal for at least twenty years. Should the borrower die or the property be sold, the principal money, and interest thereon, would immediately become repayable to the council.

The Rating (Disabled Persons) Act 1978 requires rating authorities to give rebates on the rates due in respect of certain facilities required to meet the needs of a disabled person living at home. The basic concept is that, if a disabled person needs some special feature or facility in his house which would not have been essential for him if he were not disabled, then he, or the rateable occupier of the dwelling, should be entitled to relief, broadly, to the extent of the rates attributable to the special feature or extra accommodation. Examples of facilities especially needed because of disability and eligible for a disablement rebate are:

  i altered or additional room

 ii additional bathroom

iii additional lavatory

iv central heating system serving 2 or more rooms

 v garage, carport or parking space.

2 Minor adaptations

2.1 Definition

There is a fine distinction between minor and major adaptations, and this distinction can vary from one local authority to another. Generally speaking, minor adaptations are regarded as work of a non-structural nature, which can be installed or removed without undue disturbance to the occupant.

The joint government circular entitled *Adaptations of housing for people who are physically handicapped* (see Chapter 1 p3) gives guidance to UK local authorities in its Appendices 1 and 2. They give examples of features which may be regarded as becoming part of the dwelling and, accordingly, eligible for housing subsidiy, and those which may be regarded as non-structural and, therefore, ineligible.

The following chapters of this book consider these features in detail. This chapter, in particular, looks at miscellaneous minor adaptations, although some of these will require structural fixing. Note that all metric dimensions are conversions from imperial, and have been rounded up for simplicity.

2.2 Support rails

Mobility in the home can be facilitated if appropriate support rails are provided in strategic positions. These can be more conveniently defined as:

  i grab-handles: for short lengths up to 300mm (1ft 0in)

  ii grab-rails: for intermediate lengths up to 1200mm (4ft 0in) in any one direction

iii handrails: for lengths over 1200mm (4ft 0in)

Grab-handles and rails are made of either chromed or plastic-coated steel, and can be purchased 'off the shelf' in standard lengths and shapes, or made to measure for any given situation. Support rails should satisfy two criteria:

i they must be securely fixed, because a disabled or elderly person will put more weight on them than an able-bodied person

ii they must be fixed in the correct position and at the correct height for the individual user.

Handrails are usually made of timber and fixed on to staircases or along walls in corridors or passages. Handrails should satisfy four criteria:

i they must be securely fixed, as mentioned above, but, if this is not possible on a wall surface, a floor fixing with balusters is a possibility

ii they must be fixed at the correct height, which, for an average adult, is 840mm to 1000mm (2ft 9in to 3ft 3in)

iii their size and shape must be suitable for the particular disability of the user. Handrail sections are commercially available or can be made up in a variety of profiles. A design suitable for most disabled people should enable them to grasp the entire circumference of the rail, which should have no awkward shapes or corners

iv where practicable, the rails should stretch sufficiently beyond the point where they are needed to be grasped by the user before he actually negotiates the point of difficulty.

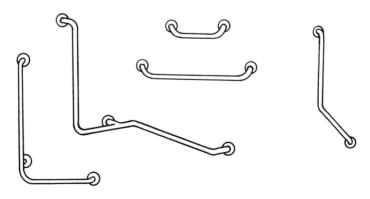

1 Grab-handles and rails of various lengths and shapes

Support rails are generally provided in juxtaposition to sanitary fittings (see also Chapter 6 p78), doorways and steps, and in any place where balance may be temporarily impaired. Where support is required some distance from the wall face, hinged rails can be provided which fold away vertically or sideways.

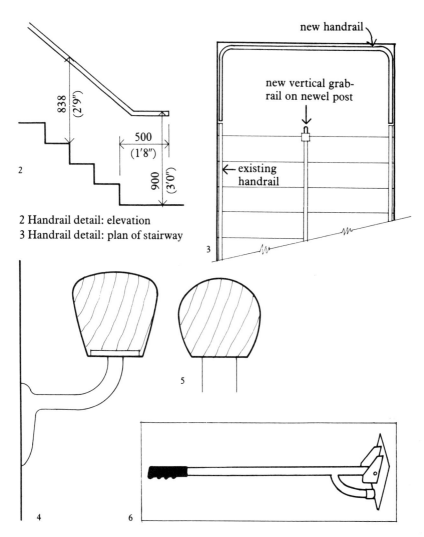

new handrail

new vertical grab-rail on newel post

← existing handrail

838 (2'9")

500 (1'8")

900 (3'0")

2

2 Handrail detail: elevation
3 Handrail detail: plan of stairway

3

5

4

6

4, 5 Typical sections through handrails

6 Vertical fold-away grab-rail

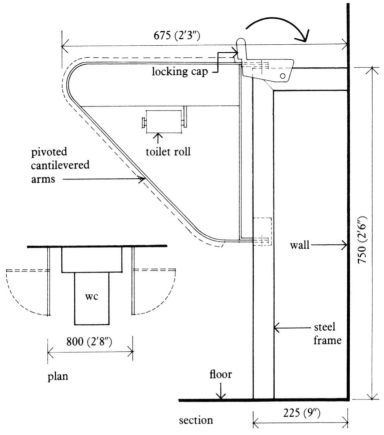

675 (2'3")

locking cap

pivoted
cantilevered
arms

toilet roll

wall

750 (2'6")

wc

steel
frame

800 (2'8")

plan

floor

section

225 (9")

7 Horizontally folding grab-rails for use in conjunction with wc

Where handrails are required on steps or stairs for people with
poor balance, it is helpful to have a handrail fitted on both sides.
This is particularly important for a person whose body is affected
on one side by a disability such as hemiplegia, who may find that
he is unable to ascend or descend the stairs according to which
side is body is affected.

2.3 Doors

In addition to the problems encountered when entering a front
door (see Chapter 3 p36), the disabled also experience difficulty
with existing internal doors because they are not wide enough,

8 Support rails which can be folded away to one or both sides of wc

their positioning is unsatisfactory or their ironmongery is unsuit-able. Most domestic doors are 762mm (2ft 6in) wide, but the net width is reduced to approximately 711mm (2ft 4in) when the door thickness (when the door is open at 90°), and the rebated profile of the door frame, are taken into account. Consequently, there is little margin for error when a wheelchair, 635mm (2ft 1in) wide, is being pushed through the door! Where the door must be approached from an angle, the door opening will have to be considerably wider than for a straight approach.

If an existing door needs widening, some thought must be given to *which* side of the frame should be altered. The difference for wheelchair access can be significant. It is possible that, when

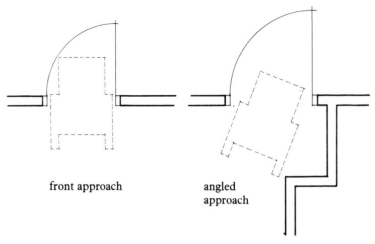

front approach

angled
approach

9 Door widths and wheelchair approaches

a wider door is being fitted, a change in the direction of opening might help to overcome any difficulties.

Hinged doors can be modified to make them easier to operate. Robust lever handles can be substituted for circular knobs, so that those with hand impairments can use forearm or elbow. Closing can be made easier if rising butts are fitted, so that the door closes gently of its own accord; alternatively, a pull handle can be fitted on the trailing face of the door. More sophisticated technical aids are delayed-action closers and, for people disabled in all four limbs, electro-mechanical gearing can be installed, which is operated by pressure pads or photo-electric cells.

Aluminium or plastic kicking-plates fitted to the trailing face of the door at the correct height will help to protect the door from damage from walking aids or wheelchair footplates. Additional protection for the base of the frame may also be justifiable on frequently used doorways.

There is a common misconception that sliding doors are easier for a disabled person to operate than hinged ones. In fact, they should only be installed where space is restricted and a hinged door would impede access or wheelchair circulation, such as small bathrooms or cloakrooms. Generally speaking, sliding doors are more draughty than hinged doors and can become misaligned, causing the lock to fail and not engage properly. In the Inner London area, the GLC drainage by-laws require that wc

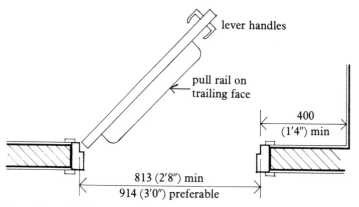

lever handles

pull rail on
trailing face

400
(1′4″) min

813 (2′8″) min
914 (3′0″) preferable

10 Hinged door detail

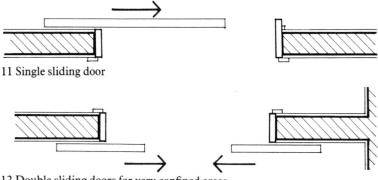

11 Single sliding door

12 Double sliding doors for very confined areas

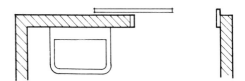

13 Sliding door located outside room to overcome obstacles

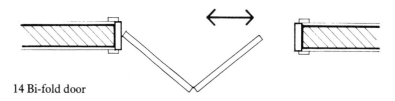

14 Bi-fold door

doors should be self-closing but, as this presents insuperable problems with sliding doors, it is possible to obtain a relaxation of this requirement.

Sliding doors can be fitted either singly or in pairs, depending on the width of the opening or the space available each side. Alternatively, bi-fold doors can be fitted, which are light in weight and easy to operate by those with hand impairments.

2.4 Electrics

Switched power points and light switches must be designed and positioned so that they can be easily reached and operated. Traditional light switches can be replaced by either the ceiling pull-cord type, possibly fitted with a suitable ring handle, or by a 'rocker plate' switch, operated by the elbow or shoulder. Power points, placed unobtrusively near the skirting board, should be repositioned at a conveniently higher level. (This will involve some 'making good' where the power point was previously fixed).

2.5 Heating

Whether a house is purpose-built or adapted, it should be sufficiently heated, because a disabled person, often less mobile and agile than an able-bodied one, may feel the cold more. Some

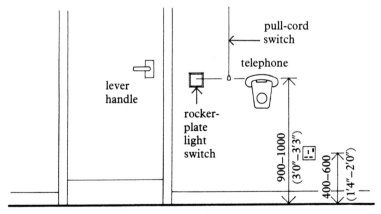

15 Positions of electrical fittings for wheelchair users

form of background or central heating in all accessible rooms is preferable, with local fires or heaters to boost individual room temperatures, as desired. The boiler controls and thermostats should be easily accessible. Provided that the dwelling is adequately insulated against heat loss by double glazing, cavity and ceiling insulation, draught stripping etc, the heating bills need not be significantly higher than for any other dwelling. Grant aid from the local authority is obtainable only for insulating the loft. (see also Chapter 1 p10).

2.6 Meters

Gas and electricity meters should, if possible, be visible to the disabled person; and coin-in-the-slot meters must, of course, be with easy reach.

2.7 Windows

The question of window controls is arguably the most difficult of all problems associated with the built environment, and the need for window modification will depend largely upon the design and position of the existing windows in a particular room. In order to advise on adapting window controls, it will be necessary for the architect or OT to know:

i whether the disabled occupant lives alone. If not, the windows could, as a last resort, be controlled by others

ii whether there is more than one window to the room requiring ventilation. The Building Regulations demand that the total area of ventilation be not less than one-twentieth of the floor area of the room so it may, therefore, transpire that only one window, or part of it, need be openable

iii the design of the existing window. Windows with side-hung casements present little problem in their existing state, provided the handles are accessible. Vertically-hung sash windows are more difficult, but a possible solution would be to screw the top sash shut, and fit pulleys and cords to operate the lower sash

iv the extent of the disability of the occupant. Top-hung vents can be controlled by fitting Rotaflex winding gear, and high-level louvres can be operated by an extension arm. However, if the occupant is disabled in all four limbs, even these innovations might prove unusable. The problem of pulling curtains may be overcome by a pulley system with cord control fitted as an integral part of the curtain tracking, a system not confined to the homes of disabled people.

If the disabled person is house-bound during the day, and there is an interesting view from the window, the sill height should be low enough for the disabled person to see out easily when sitting down. An existing window can be replaced by a new, taller window with lower-level sill. Alternatively, a high-silled window can be enlarged by inserting a new 'sub-light' beneath it, but bulky transom or balcony rails which obstruct vision should be avoided.

2.8 Safety

Poor balance, and lack of strength and co-ordination may result in physically disabled or elderly people being more prone than the able-bodied to falls and other accidents in the home. Support rails to assist tricky operations such as bathing (see Chapter 4 p54) or stair-climbing (see figure 3) can help to alleviate potential dangers. The risk of personal injury can be lessened by obvious features such as non-slip flooring, adequate lighting, particularly to stairs and external doors, sensibly designed furniture, and a generally tidy house. The degree of injury inflicted is also affected by what a person falls on and, in many cases, chamfering or rounding-off of sharp corners is all that is needed. Nevertheless, a compromise has to be reached between complete safety and maintaining a homely environment.

2.9 Hoists

If the disabled person has limited use of his arms and no use of his legs, mechanical lifting aids to assist with transfers are usually installed. The OT will usually make the assessment and give consideration as to whether the hoist will be operated by the user himself or by an attendant. The overhead type of hoist consists of an electrically-operated control unit with lifting tape, spreader bar and sling underneath, which can be raised, lowered, or moved forwards or backwards by the operator. The control unit is hung from steel tracking, securely fixed to the underside of the

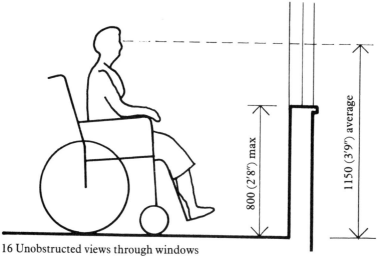

800 (2'8") max

1150 (3'9") average

16 Unobstructed views through windows

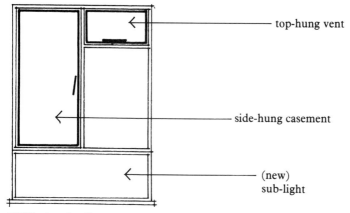

top-hung vent

side-hung casement

(new)
sub-light

17 Window detail

18 Curved aluminium section to external
corners of walls

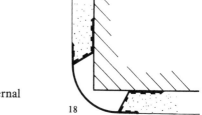

18

ceiling, which may, in some cases, entail refixing the light fittings.

The position of the tracking is of prime importance, in order that a safe transfer can be made. In the bathroom, the track will need to pass over the centre of the bath and about one metre (3ft 3in) away from the taps. Over the wc, the track must pass above the centre of the bowl. In the bedroom, it should pass over the point on the bed where the user's hips will be when he is lying on the bed. The tracking should, preferably, be fitted across the joists rather than parallel to them, because the loading will then be distributed more evenly over the whole ceiling area. Where the ceiling is not strong enough, or in cases of short-term need, a portable steel gantry frame can be used. This does not, however, enhance the décor of the room and can obstruct windows and doorways.

If a ceiling track is not fitted wall-to-wall, stops must be incorporated at each end to prevent the accidental slipping-off of the control unit. Fixed hoists need a 13amp electricity supply, controls which are accessible to the operator, a 'step-down' transformer (when installed in a bathroom) and a recoil drum to

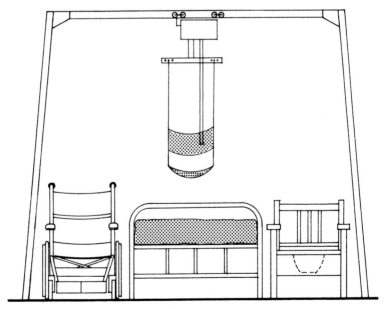

19 Overhead hoist on steel gantry frame

prevent the supply cable from getting entangled with equipment.

Where tracking has to extend to adjoining rooms, the section of wall over the door lintel must be omitted. This is best done by building in a storey-height frame and hanging a taller door. A conventional sliding door cannot be fitted here, because the tracking required for the door would collide with the workings of the hoist. However, this problem can be overcome, if a pair of sliding doors is fitted with a central notch cut for the tracking to pass through.

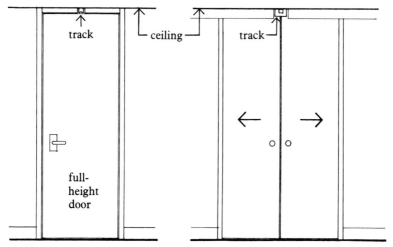

20, 21 Hoist track details

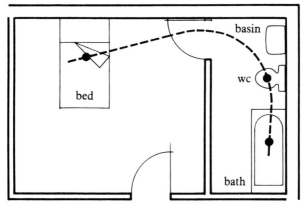

22 Layout of typical hoist installation

23

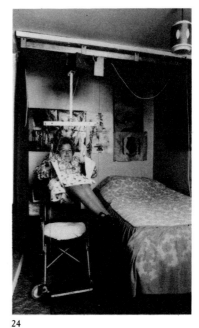

24

23 Multi-directional ceiling track with re-coil drum

24 Short length of ceiling track from wall to wall

25

25 Portable hoists (cannot be used independently)

Portable hoists, which can be dismantled and stored in the back of a car, perform more or less the same function as those mentioned above. They cannot be used independently, and other members of the family must, therefore, be involved in their operation. The need for structural adaptations is considerably reduced, but doorways and passages must be wide enough to facilitate the movement of the hoists. Bath panels may have to be modified to enable the projecting feet of the hoist to be pushed underneath.

2.10 Kitchens

When an existing kitchen is adapted, every detail must be scrutinised, if inconvenience and accidents are to be averted. The room can either be stripped bare and purpose-built units fitted, or the existing units can be added to or altered. If the kitchen was badly planned originally, some structural alterations may have to be carried out first. Obviously, the experience of both the architect and OT is particularly valuable in such a case.

Storage facilities in the kitchen present many problems for ambulant disabled people, as well as wheelchair users. All storage zones need to be at heights which can be conveniently reached. Inaccessible areas can only be successfully utilised by

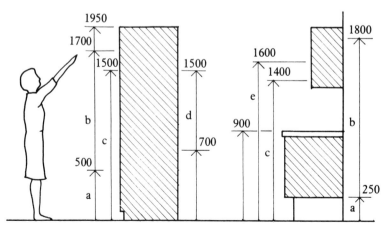

26 Reach zones for able-bodied person: a = low reach; b = high reach; c = reach to back of 300mm shelf; d = preferred zone; e = high reach over 600 mm obstruction; permitted zone for general use 250mm to 1800mm

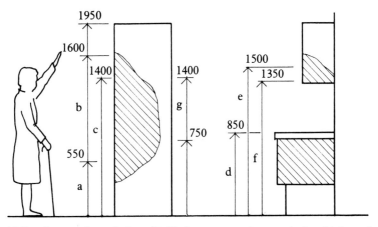

27 Reach zones for ambulant disabled person: a = low reach; b = high reach; c = reach to back of 300mm shelf; d = worktop; e = high reach over 600mm obstruction; f = reach to back of 200mm shelf; g = preferred zone

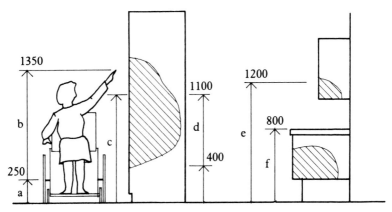

28 Reach zones for wheelchair user: a = low reach; b = high reach; c = reach to back of shelf; d = preferred zone; e = high reach over obstruction; f = work top

able-bodied members of the family or, occasionally, by the disabled person if equipped with a reaching aid. Zones for storage become more restricted as physical ability deteriorates, and figures 26 to 28 illustrate accessible zones for storage for the able-bodied, ambulant disabled and wheelchair disabled people.

Figures 32 and 33 show that the height of working surfaces for wheelchair users needs to be lower than normal, 800mm (2ft 8in) being acceptable in most cases. What is less often appreciated, however, is that worktop heights for some ambulant disabled people, such as back sufferers, should be *higher* than normal, not lower.

In an existing kitchen, it might be uneconomic or impracticable to install new purpose-made units throughout. The desirability of lower-level units throughout is questionable if the kitchen is shared by able-bodied members of the family. Instead, individual worktops can be incorporated, specifically designed for the disabled user. Apart from lower-level worktops, kitchen units for wheelchair users must have adequate knee-space underneath – the cupboards below can be omitted, or the work-surface itself extended by pull-out sections.

Sink units can be installed which have shallow bowls giving knee-space below, without the rim's being too high for comfort. Sink taps frequently need to be modified to help overcome the handicap of poor grip or reach limitations; however, the fitting of certain types of specialised tap may require the consent of the water authority. Standard pillar taps can be replaced by lever taps, but the choice of these should take into account the degree of heavy-handed use to which they would be subjected.

For those who find reaching difficult, the water supply can be operated by remote-control lever taps fitted on the front of the sink unit. Where lifting is a greater problem than reaching, a swivel tap can be placed off-centre, so that utensils can be filled without their being lifted out of the sink.

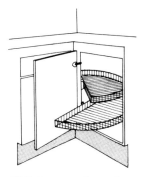

29 Swing-out wire racks

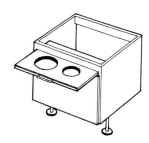

30 Storage unit with pull-out work surface

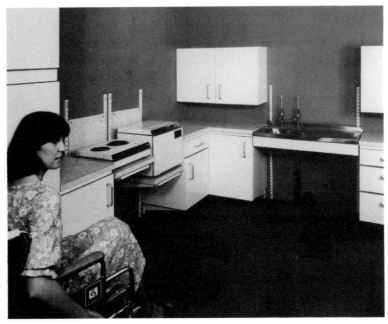

31 Purpose-built kitchen units for wheelchair user

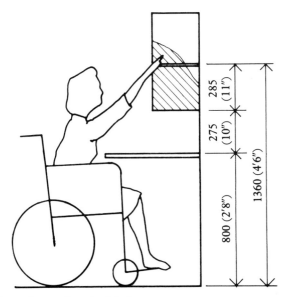

32 High reach zone for wheelchair user

Existing base units can be modified by installing slide-out wire racks or semicircular trays which swing out, to prevent the need for over-reaching for items placed at the back. Mobile drawer units or trolleys on castors can provide an additional work-surface and enable equipment to be carried.

If a disabled person lives alone or is at home for most of the day, the kitchen may be used for eating in, because it is the warmest room in the house. It would, therefore, be desirable to build some form of low-level breakfast bar unit or to make sure that there is sufficient floor space to include a kitchen table, so that travel and carrying distances are kept to a minimum.

Many housewives are reluctant to part with their tried and trusted cookers, but the conventional cooker is not designed for wheelchair users. The oven is too low, the rings are too high and the controls at the back are dangerously inaccessible. Where their is sufficient space, the cooker can be exchanged for a split-level model where the height of the oven door can be adjusted. Although a separate hob takes up more space, when it is fitted on the worktop, it allows someone with weak hands to slide utensils on to the hob rings from the adjacent work surface. For disabled people with poor grip or poor sight, special cooker

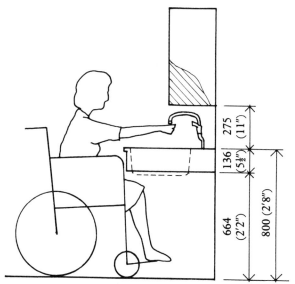

33 Sink position for wheelchair user

34 Lever taps (should be able to withstand heavy-handed use)

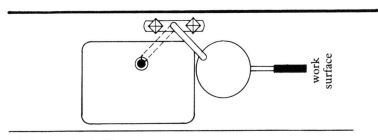

35 Swivel tap fixed off-centre

36 Mobile trolley

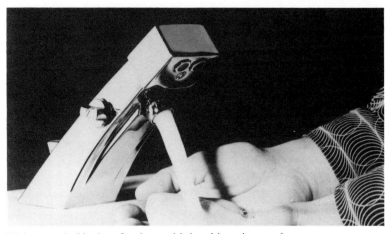

37 Automatic Magitap for those with hand impairments*

38 Remote control Leva taps fitted to front of adjustable-height sink unit

control knobs are available from gas/electricity authorities.

Automatic washing machines, tumble-dryers and dishwashers are a comparative luxury for the able-bodied housewife, but these machines may become necessities if she is disabled. Floor space should be allocated for these appliances, together with the necessary electrical supplies and plumbing arrangements.

* Since going to press, this product has been discontinued.

3 Access and external works

3.1 Wheelchair access

The first obstacle a wheelchair user encounters when entering a building is access through the front door. The Building Regulations require, under normal circumstances, that the outer damp-proof course (dpc) be not less than 150mm (6in) above the adjoining ground level, which means that a step of at least 200mm (8in) has to be negotiated.

In new housing for disabled people, this step need be no problem if the internal floor is constructed at the same level as the outside ground, as long as adequate precautions are taken not to bridge the dpc. However, in the case of existing dwellings, an external ramp must be used to overcome these differences in levels.

3.2 Ramps

It should not be assumed that a ramp is required by every disabled person. Whilst essential for wheelchair users, a ramp could be a greater hazard than two or three broad steps to some elderly or unsure-footed people. Where it is proposed to construct a ramp outside an external door, alternative provision should be made for access by able-bodied people, whether members of the household or callers.

The ramp should be sited so that it does not trip up those unaware of its existence (eg visitors, tradesmen) and, therefore, cause more hardship than it was intended to alleviate. The sides and bottom edge could be made more conspicuous if painted white or yellow. A ramp should be placed so that it does not encroach upon or obstruct a right of way. If this does happen, a

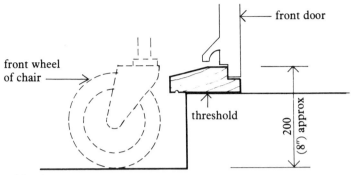

39 Typical detail of step to domestic front door

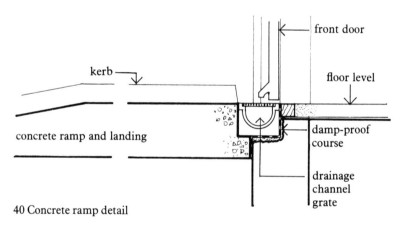

40 Concrete ramp detail

portable ramp, should be used, which can be removed and stored after use.

The England and Wales Building Regulations provide that the gradient of a permanent ramp should not be steeper than 1:12, whether it is to be used by wheelchair users or not. Where a ramp is exceptionally long, say, 5000mm (16ft 8in) or over, the gradient may have to be reduced to 1:20 and 'breather' landings incorporated at points where the ramp changes direction. A lengthy ramp can be contained in the garden much more easily if it is multi-directional. The same ramp, if straight, might be longer than the garden itself or protrude an unacceptable distance away from the house.

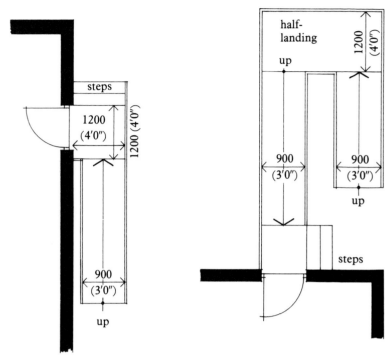

41, 42 Typical ramp layouts

The steepness of the gradient that can be negotiated depends on the length of the ramp. A steep gradient that may be acceptable on a short ramp will be too steep on a longer one. A chair-bound person, with strong upper limbs, may find short ramps of 1:10, or steeper, little or no problem. All external ramps, whatever their length or gradient, should have a landing at the top, so that the disabled person can park his wheelchair on a level surface whilst opening, closing or locking the outside door.

External ramps affording easy access into buildings can be either:

  i permanent

 ii movable

iii portable.

A permanent ramp is usually made of concrete with a surface either textured or sprinkled with carborundum dust to provide extra grip. Concrete ramps will last the lifetime of the building and should therefore be designed carefully to blend in with the surroundings, possibly by making up the ground level each side. Despite its advantages, concrete is comparatively cheap, lends itself to complex shapes and can be laid almost immediately. For short term need, ramps should be movable ie capable of assembly or dismantling in a couple of hours, without unduly disturbing the ground surface. These ramps are usually made of angle iron with inlaid surfaces of expanded metal or felt-covered marine plywood. Handrails can also be fitted as an optional extra, if required.

Portable ramps consist mainly of inverted metal channel sections used as a pair, which fold at mid-span. Some types have carrying handles and can be carried inside a car, so that they can be laid down and taken up after use outside different buildings. However, the help of an attendant may be needed if these ramps are to be fully utilised.

Kerbs for the exposed edge of a ramp are usually essential, to prevent wheelchair wheels from accidentally slipping off. Kerbs should be at least 75mm (3in) high and substantial enough not to disintegrate or break way.

The minimum width of a ramp should be 900mm (3ft 0in) inside the kerbs, although 1000mm (3ft 3in) would be preferable. Where there are landings to provide changes in direction, the width should be increased to 1200mm (4ft 0in), to make it easy for the wheelchair to be manoeuvred.

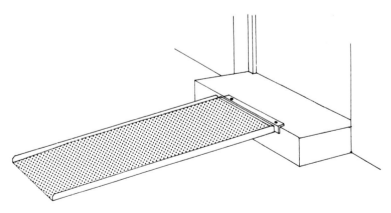

43 Proprietary movable ramp bolted to doorstep

44 Movable ramp with integral edge kerbs to provide strength

45 Movable ramp of glass-fibre construction

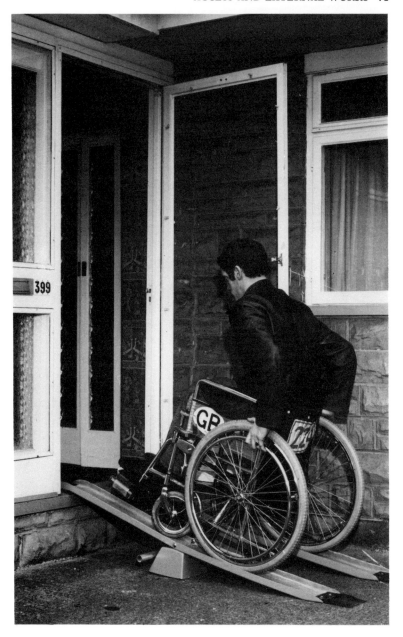

46 Portable ramps: useful temporary measure when visiting other buildings

In some situations, the gradient of the ramp is determined, not only by the fixed levels at each end, but also by the length. However, if the resulting gradient is obviously too steep for the disabled person to manage on his own or aided by an attendant, an external lift may have to be installed.

If space is severely restricted, a scissor-action step lift can be used. It consists of a platform large enough to accommodate a wheelchair and can be raised or lowered by an electrically-operated bellows unit.

Once up the ramp, the next obstacle the wheelchair user must overcome is the threshold across the doorway. This bulky timber section can be removed and a low-level proprietary aluminium threshold fitted, with an integral rubber insert. Additional protection can also be provided by a weather-bar or outside drainage channel to combat the penetration of driving rain. An internal kicking-plate can be fitted to the bottom of the door to conceal any blocking-out necessary because the original threshold has been removed.

It is obviously necessary for a disabled driver to park his car as near to the front door of his house as possible. Any vehicle parked on the public highway is exposed to the elements and may cause an obstruction. Therefore, off-street parking of some description is desirable.

Where a disabled driver lives in a flat or mid-terrace house, and vehicular access to the garden is impossible, the car must be parked in the nearest safest place. If this affects local traffic flow, a small lay-by can be constructed, or a reserved car-space be allocated, duly marked and signposted. However, this facility can only be provided where parking restrictions, such as yellow lines, are already in force, so that the reserved space is officially recognised and its unauthorised use by others is an offence. In other cases, the disabled driver will have to make his own arrangements, based on the goodwill of his neighbours.

3.3 Cross-overs

Off-street parking within the curtilage of a dwelling will involve crossing the public footpath and laying some form of driveway or hardstanding. The cost of this work is not, however, covered by grant aid as described in Chapter 1 p9.

The Highways Act 1980 states that 'where the occupier of any

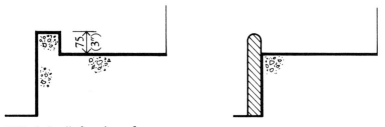

47 Kerb details for edges of ramps

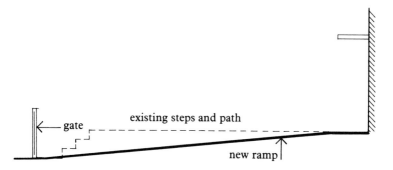

48 Section of ramp, with fixed levels at ends, to replace existing steps and path

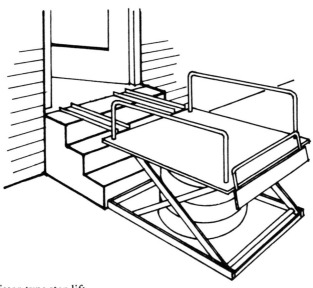

49 Scissor-type step lift

premises adjoining the highway habitually takes a vehicle across the grassed verge or footpath, the local authority can serve a notice to impose conditions on its use or, alternatively, construct a proper cross-over and recover the cost from the occupier'. Planning permission will also be necessary if the cross-over is required to provide access on to a classified trunk road.

Section 20 of the Chronically Sick and Disabled Persons Act 1970 removes restrictions on invalid carriages mounting or using footpaths, but this concession applies only to lightweight vehicles less than 113kg (250lb), and not capable of more than 4mph (The Use of Invalid Carriages on Highways Regulations 1970).

Some makes of electrically-powered invalid chair are capable of climbing low kerbs and the Vessa power-chairs can be fitted with a kerb-climbing attachment. This lifts the smaller front wheels over the kerb and rolls the chair forward, so that the rear wheels with their direct drive have sufficient power to lift the wheelchair and occupant up the kerb.

3.4 Gates

Gates should, if possible, be dispensed with but, if they are kept for reasons of safety or appearance, they must not open outwards and obstruct the footpath or highway (Highways Act 1980).

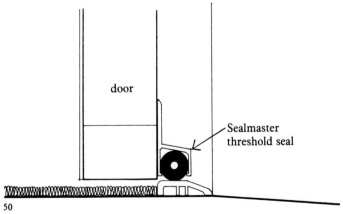

door

Sealmaster threshold seal

50

50, 51 Low-level thresholds for wheelchair user

52 Wheelchair fitted with a kerb climbing attachment

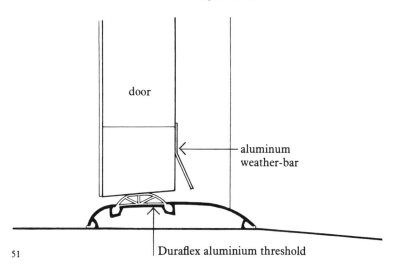

door

aluminum
weather-bar

Duraflex aluminium threshold

51

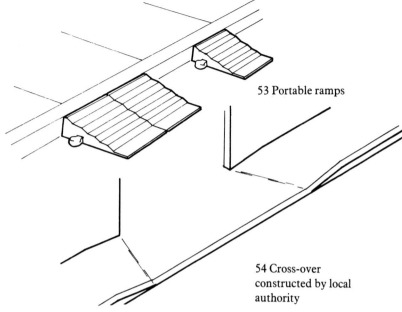

53 Portable ramps

54 Cross-over
constructed by local
authority

3.5 Drives

Vehicular drives can be laid out in a variety of designs, according
to the size and shape of the garden. Unless the disabled person's
property faces onto a quiet residential road or cul-de-sac, a
turning space should be provided, so that the car does not have to
be reversed in from, or out onto, the road.

The most common material for constructing drives and hard-
standings is concrete, because it is comparatively cheap. However, other materials, such as tarmacadam or gravel, are more
visually attractive and so blend more sympathetically into the
garden scene.

3.6 Garages

Where a lock-up garage exists but is of insufficient size to enable
a wheelchair user to transfer from wheelchair to car and vice
versa, the garage is almost impossible to use. If a new purpose-
built garage is designed, it must be large enough for wheelchair
transfers. If a disabled driver uses two wheelchairs, one at home
and one at his destination, a lock-up garage would protect the
empty wheelchair from bad weather or theft.

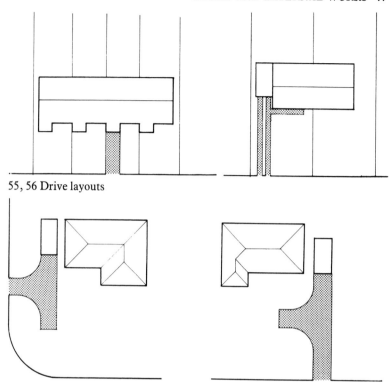

55, 56 Drive layouts

57, 58 Drive layouts with turning spaces

If the disabled driver is ambulant or it is the housewife who is disabled, a carport may be a preferable alternative to a garage. In such an area close to the house, the washing can be hung to dry if the housewife has no tumble-dryer (see also Chapter 2 p35).

Access to the garage or carport from the house should, if possible, be under cover, and artificially lit if used at night. Integral garages, or those which abut the main wall of the house, can be fitted with an interconnecting door. In order to comply with the Building Regulations, this door should be fire-resistant, self-closing, and have a step up of 100mm (4in); this can be negotiated if an internal ramp is provided.

3.7 Garage equipment

Optional extras fitted in appropriate positions can make it easier for the disabled person to use the garage. A chain monkey-pull fitted to the roof may make the transfer from chair to car-seat easier. A two-way switch to the light should be fitted and a 13amp power point is necessary for trickle-charging batteries of electrically-operated cars or wheelchairs. Up-and-over garage doors are more convenient than the double-leaf hinged type, but many wheelchair users find that doors electrically operated by remote control provide the only satisfactory solution.

3.8 Gardens

Many disabled people find a garden a liability or even an embarrassment, but others find that gardening is therapeutic and provides them with the exercise necessary to help them to recover gradually or prevent their existing condition from deteriorating. Gardening can provide the psychological escape everyone seeks from time to time. Even if the disabled person himself is not a keen gardener, provision should be made for him to be able to sit outside, on sunny days, while reading or doing sedentary work. A garden may be the disabled child's only play-area and it must be easily accessible from the house and separated from any potential dangers, such as road traffic or fish ponds.

Social-service authorities in the UK rarely finance garden alterations and such work is not eligible for grant aid. In most cases, the work is carried out by the occupant or his relatives.

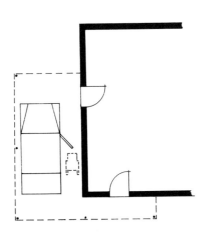

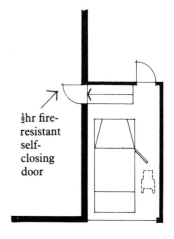

½hr fire-
resistant
self-
closing
door

59 Car port with covered way to external door

60 Attached garage with internal ramp

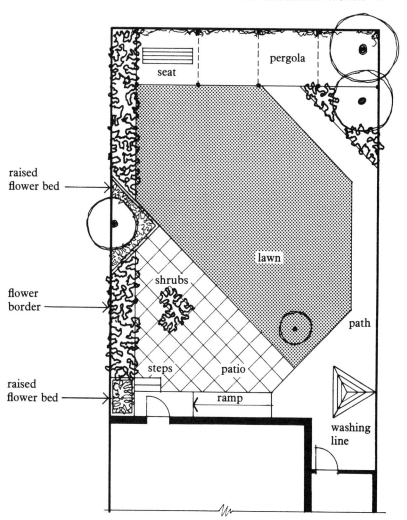

61 Garden layout suitable for wheelchair user

Disabled people can now undertake many gardening operations with the aid of specially designed or adapted garden tools. However, a well-laid-out garden is an obvious prerequisite. Figure 61 illustrates a flower garden suitable for a wheelchair user.

The garden should be surrounded by a wide uncluttered path with gentle slopes to accommodate changes in level, although broad steps are preferable for the ambulant disabled. Flower beds should be narrow, to make cultivation easy but, for people with reach problems, flower beds could be raised with the aid of retaining walls or by the use of tubs placed on the patio.

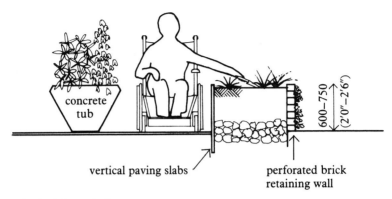

concrete tub

600–750 (2'0"–2'6")

vertical paving slabs

perforated brick retaining wall

62 Raised flower beds

A permanent water pipe laid beside the garden path is the simplest method of irrigation, although the increase in water rates needs to be taken into account. Cutting the grass from a wheelchair is less of a problem when using a hover-type motor mower, and a sit-on type of mower is ideal for large gardens with extensive lawns. If traditional linear-type washing lines are unsuitable, rotary lines can be used. The height of the line should be lowered to suit the needs of the chair-bound housewife.

The Disabled Living Foundation Garden Advisory Service and the relevant publications listed in the Bibliography (see p128) can provide further information on the preceding five paragraphs.

4 Baths and showers

4.1 Scope of choice

Many disabled people find the task of using a conventional bath too difficult to contemplate or just impossible. An 'all-over wash' could be the only answer for someone so severely handicapped that any kind of bathing is too hazardous. The washing can either be done independently or with the assistance of a health visitor or member of the family.

Disabled people who can use a conventional bath may find it more difficult to get out than to get in. A bench seat at the end of the bath, level with the top – normally used on conjunction with an inside bath-seat – can help to make this operation easier. Some designs of bath-seats are not recommended for use with glass-fibre or acrylic baths.

Where a conventional bath is needed for other members of the family, various additional aids for the benefit of the disabled or elderly relative can be introduced. Plate 67 shows a selection of aids which can be used in an average domestic bathroom; an OT could recommend *which* of these aids should be used in any particular situation. There is insufficient space in this book to catalogue all the aids which might be helpful, but further information can be obtained from the Disabled Living Foundation. Acrylic bath-liners, moulded for a shallow-seated position, can be fitted on a conventional bath and removed after use, if required. These liners are particularly useful for children and save the parent from having to bend over too far.

In addition to overhead electric hoists (Chapter 2 p24), mechanical hoists, operated either by the user or a helper, can be fitted to the floor, near to the existing bath. Most types have a water-proof chair or sling in which the user can sit while bathing.

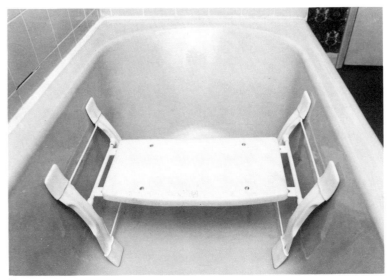

63

63 Inset type of bath seat

64, 65 Acrylic bath-liners of varying profiles to suit child or adult

64   65

66 Mechanical swivel hoist used in conjunction with traditional bath

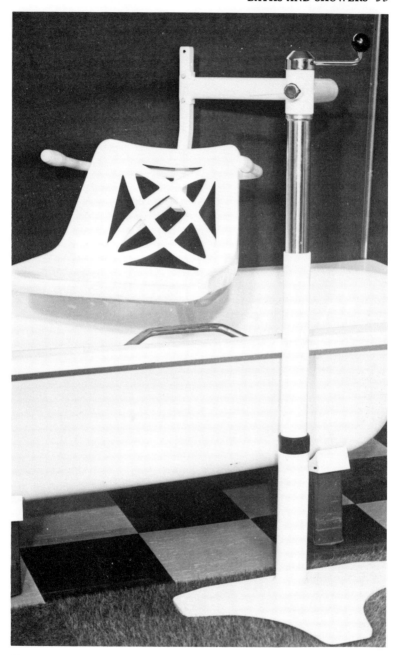

67 Selection of bathroom aids (see p51)

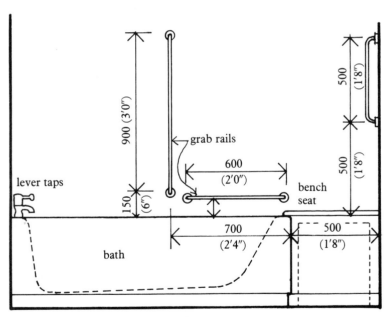

68 Aids used in conjunction with bath

69 The compact Medic-bath which can now be fitted with sliding seat to facilitate wheelchair transfer

Bathing in the seated position can be carried out in a tub-type bath, such as the Medic-bath. It is mainly used where a nurse can be in attendance, such as in homes for the elderly. The sliding seat fitment is an optional extra and is useful for transferring from wheelchairs. The unit has the advantage of being very compact, measuring a mere 895mm by 680mm (3ft 0in by 2ft 3in). It is essential that the room in which the bath is installed be effectively heated, because the user sits, undressed, inside the tub while it is being filled with the desired amount of water.

Where space permits, the Cleveland shower bath can provide an alternative solution to the bathing problem. The user sits on the swivel stool (by transferring from the wheelchair, if necessary) and pushes backwards to transfer on to the integral bath-seat. The stool is then pushed out of the bath, the door slotted in and the shower-curtain pulled round. If the disabled user has weak upper limbs or is obese, he may find it difficult to use this equipment unaided.

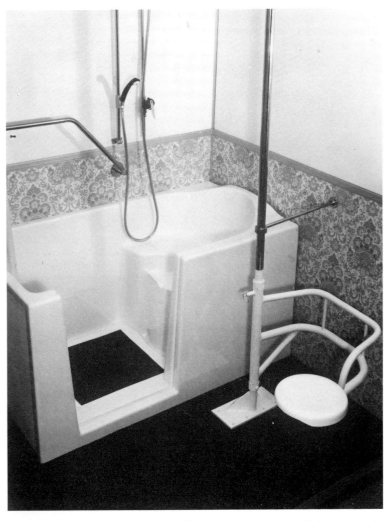

70 Cleveland shower bath with glass-fibre tub, swivel stool and shower attachment

Where a disabled person is living alone, the existing bath can be removed and a shower substituted, if both the disabled person and the OT think that this is the best solution. However, if there are other people in the house, they may prefer the bath to remain for their own use. Since most bathrooms are small, it is often difficult to decide where to put the new shower.

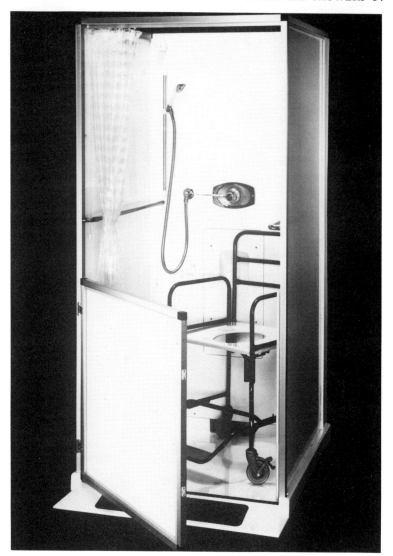

71 Chiltern shower cubicle

Sometimes, it can be installed in a cubicle in the corner of a
bedroom, or it may be possible to install it above the existing
bath. One definite advantage of a cubicle is that it is completely
enclosed and, if a roof is fitted, condensation in the rest of the
room will be alleviated.

It is important that any shower cubicle or shower area be fitted with strong support rails in strategic positions (see also Chapter 2 p15). The ambulant disabled person will find these necessary when stepping over the rim of the shower-tray, and the wheelchair user will find them essential when transferring from chair to shower-seat. Sufficient grab-rails should be an integral part of glass-fibre cubicles when purchased, as they cannot normally be fitted afterwards.

The most sophisticated shower cubicle designed with the disabled person in mind is probably the Chiltern. The bather can be wheeled into the cubicle on a shower chair and an attendant can help, if necessary, by using the hand-spray attachment over the half-door. This door incorporates a rubber water-seal and the thermostatic anti-scald shower is activated by a pull cord. Installation is comparatively simple, the shower being plumbed in, with flexible supplies and waste pipe. Since the drainage is pumped out, the height of the outlet is not governed by the existing plumbing in the house.

A solution often adopted to ease the problem of space is to site the shower unit above the existing wc, if the floor is of 'solid' construction. The disabled person can then use the wc as a

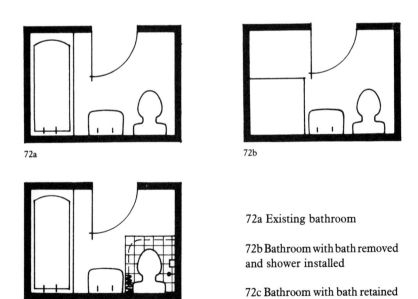

72a

72b

72c

72a Existing bathroom

72b Bathroom with bath removed and shower installed

72c Bathroom with bath retained and shower installed over wc shower-seat, and the floor around is curtained off and relaid with quarry tiles, to a fall into a waste trap in the floor. If a convenient place for the toilet roll cannot be found outside the shower curtain, a plastic or polythene cover can be put over it, to protect it while the shower is in operation.

Where a wc is separate from the bathroom, or a new wc is being provided on the ground floor, the shower can be placed overhead in the same way. The space necessary for drying and dressing must also be taken into account. If the walls are fully tiled, a shower-curtain is unecessary, but careful consideration must be given to the water-bar, to prevent water from trickling underneath the door into the adjoining room.

Once the OT, disabled person and family have agreed to a shower fitting, the most suitable type of shower for that person must be chosen. A shower installed for elderly or disabled people should be thermostatically controlled and have an anti-scald cut-out device which acts immediately and not after several seconds have elapsed. Improvised shower attachments can be fitted by connecting hoses to bath taps, but these are not recom-

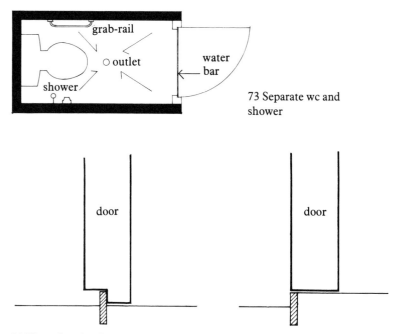

73 Separate wc and shower

74 Water-bar details

mended, because any slight variation in water pressure created by the simultaneous use of taps elsewhere in the house produces marked variations in temperature.

4.2 Shower units

Shower units used by disabled people may be either *plumbed-in* showers or *instantaneous* electric showers, both of which can be placed in cubicles, or over baths, shower trays or wcs. In all cases, the ability of the disabled person to manage the controls should be considered by the OT.

Plumbed-in showers
As the name suggests, these showers are plumbed into the existing hot and cold water supplies in the house, and a thermostatic mixer-valve controls the temperature of the spray. Depending on whether a disabled person sits or stands under the shower, the OT should advise the architect on the best position for the mixer control.

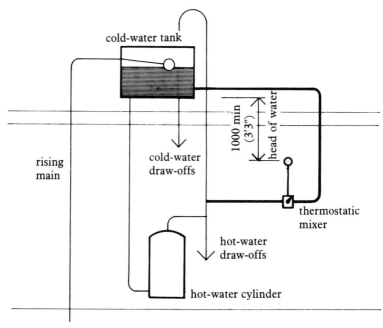

75 Diagram of plumbing for shower installation

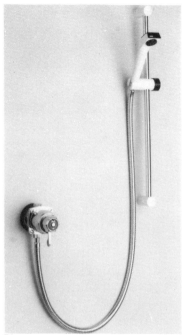

76

77

76, 77 Plumbed-in showers: these must incorporate thermostatic mixers

78

78 Instantaneous showers, requiring a supply of electricity and cold water at mains pressure

Plumbed-in showers are quite suitable if:

i the house contains a cold water tank

ii it is a practicable distance from the proposed shower

iii it is high enough to provide sufficient head of water

iv suitable hot water is laid on.

A factor to be taken into consideration is whether a boiler keeps the water in the copper cylinder hot continuously during the day, or whether an immersion heater has to be switched on every time a shower is required. In the later case, it may be more economical to install an instantaneous electric shower.

Instantaneous electric showers
In the same way that cold water can be heated to provide an intermittent supply over a kitchen sink, cold water can be electrically heated to provide warm water for a shower. Instantaneous showers are plumbed directly into the rising main and the water is heated by a 6000watt electrical element which is an integral part of the shower unit. This electrical current is only consumed, however, while the shower is in operation and, to maintain a degree of safety, some manufacturers recommend that the heating element be placed outside the shower curtain.

The electrical supply must be directly connected, via a ceiling pull-switch, to a 30amp fuse in the consumer unit. If, as is usually the case, no spare fuse exists, an extension unit, providing the extra fuseways, must be fitted by a qualified electrician. It is also advisable to seek professional guidance on the condition of the existing wiring, particularly if the property is over twenty-five years old. (See also DHSS report entitled *Instantaneous electric water heaters for shower purposes: suitability for use by disabled people.*)

4.3 Shower-trays
An ambulant disabled person often has difficulty in stepping over the rim of a conventional tray. The tray may prevent a wheelchair from being manoeuvred freely in a confined space. In these circumstances, a 'wet-floor' type of shower could be installed: this involves laying non-slip quarry tiles to falls, so that water can drain into a waste outlet in the floor. The edge of the shower area can be slightly raised to contain overflowing water,

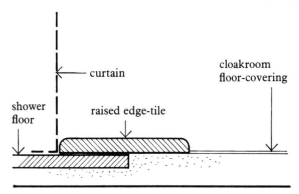

curtain

cloakroom
floor-covering

shower
floor

raised edge-tile

79 Edge detail to 'wet-floor' shower

but it should be low enough to allow a wheelchair to be manoeuvred easily. Alternatively, a proprietary glass-fibre shower
base can be installed, as long as the base is firmly supported by
timber battening, so that it can withstand the weight of a loaded
wheelchair.

A fold-away shower cabinet has been designed to overcome the
common problem of lack of space. This unit occupies the same
floor area as a wardrobe 225mm (9in) deep and unfolds to a
full-sized shower. It can be sited almost anywhere but it is only
suitable for those physically capable of unfolding it and stepping
over the rather high rim.

Where a wet-floor type of shower is required in a bathroom
with a timber suspended floor, it would be difficult to provide a
fall on the existing floorboards and there would be a risk of
timber decay if water penetrated through the floor covering. In
this situation, the best solution would be provide a sunken
shower-tray supported on new lengths of sleeper wall, as long as
careful attention is given to sealing the junction between the floor
boards and the shower-tray perimeter.

80 Cloakroom with 'wet-floor' shower, allowing
front or side wheelchair transfers to wc

81 Fold-away shower cubicle

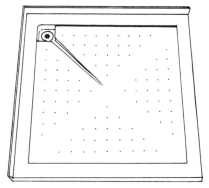

82 Proprietary glass-fibre shower tray

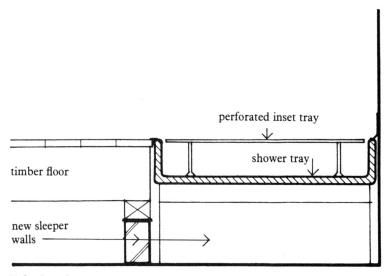

perforated inset tray

timber floor

shower tray

new sleeper
walls

83 Sunken shower tray

4.4 Shower-seats

Showers for disabled people invariably require a waterproof seat
of some kind. A portable shower chair can be supplied separ-
ately; or, alternatively, a seat can be built in as a permanent
fixture. If other members of the family want to use the shower,
the seat should fold against the wall. The OT should consult the
architect to ensure that the seat and the grab-rails are fixed in the
correct position, so that the shower can be used effectively.

4.5 Heating for shower rooms

Some disabled people are unable to keep themselves as warm as able-bodied people and it is, therefore, important that the shower room be adequately heated. Where there are no radiators, the room can be independently heated by an infra-red wall heater, providing its position and wiring conform to the current IEE regulations.

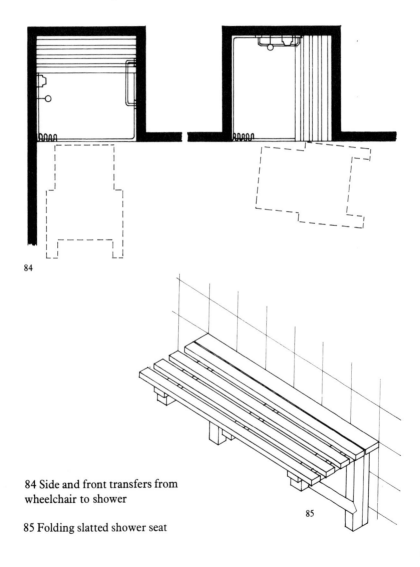

84

84 Side and front transfers from wheelchair to shower

85 Folding slatted shower seat

86 Proprietary fold-away shower seat

5 Lifts

5.1 Deciding factors

In the home, a small lift can be installed as an alternative to building an extension for a disabled person who finds stair climbing difficult or impossible. A lift not only gives the disabled person easy access to all floors in the house, but it can also be of great benefit to other members of the household.

A disabled infant can quite easily be carried up and down stairs by his parents but, as he grows heavier, a lift becomes necessary if the parents are not themselves to become disabled by the physical strain. A lift may also enable a disabled husband and wife to sleep together in an upstairs bedroom rather than on a bed-settee in the main reception room, the latter being obviously detrimental to family life, especially during periods of illness.

There are two basic types of home lift available, namely, *vertical lifts* and *stair-lifts*. The minimum safety requirements for the design, construction, installation, operation and maintenance of powered home lifts for the specific use of disabled people are laid down in the British Standards, BS 5900: 1980 and BS 5776: 1979.

The OT, the architect and the disabled person and his family should decide jointly which is the most suitable type of lift. The decision will be affected by the prognosis, the nature of the disability (whether fluctuating or not), the cost, the layout of the house and whether a wheelchair will be used.

Since the installation of a domestic lift gives the disabled person access to the existing accommodation within the house, it is in many ways a better solution than the provision of additional amenities at ground-floor level. However, if it is considered that a vertical lift occupies too much floor space in a first-floor bed-

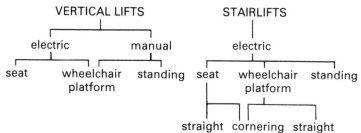

87 Diagram of selection of lift types available

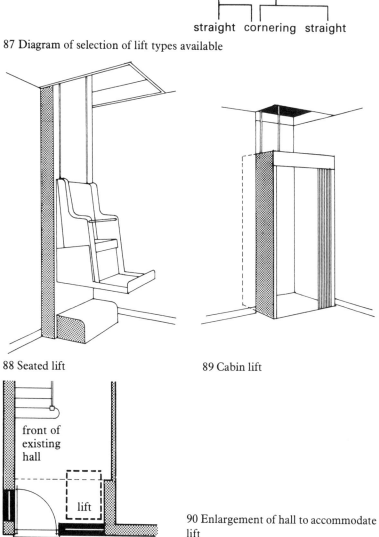

88 Seated lift

89 Cabin lift

front of
existing
hall

lift

90 Enlargement of hall to accommodate
lift

room, or that a staircase is not suitable for the installation of a stair-lift, the alternative adaptations discussed in this book may have to be considered.

The installation of a lift may seem perfectly feasible to the architect, and an eminently suitable solution to the OT, but it cannot be entertained if the disabled person or his family object on principle. Some people are afraid of mechanical contrivances, such as lifts, and the disabled person may also be sensitive about his disability and feel that a lift in his only reception room is unduly obtrusive and a constant reminder of his disability. To reassure the disabled person, the OT or social worker may suggest taking him to see or operate a similar lift recently installed in the neighbourhood.

5.2 Vertical lifts

A vertical lift consists of a cabin, seat or platform which travels on vertical guides through a purpose-made aperture in the upper floor. A cabin-type lift may be required, large enough to carry a disabled person in his wheelchair, but a vertical seat might be all that is necessary to carry an ambulant disabled person. A variety of lifts in different sizes is available.

A self-sealing trap can be incorporated in the floor so that, as the lift rises, it raises the trap clear, and then drops it back into position during its descent. In the case of cabin-type lifts, however, it is better to construct an enclosed shaft with a door at the upper-floor level which cannot be opened if the lift car is at the lower level.

The lift has a small electric motor activated by call buttons on each floor and inside the lift itself. If there is a power failure, the lift can be raised or lowered mechanically to either floor. The relevant British Standards list the various safety features which should be incorporated. These include fail-safe brakes, a sensitised platform beneath the car and safety cut-out switches around the ceiling aperture.

If the installation of a lift involves expensive building work or structural alterations, the overall feasability of the plan may have to be questioned. Figure 90 illustrates how a small hall can be enlarged to utilise the external porch so that a wheelchair can be manoeuvred more easily.

Building work of some kind must be carried out before any

type of lift is installed. This work includes making an aperture in the upper floor or forming a pit at the base of the lift and providing a 13amp power socket nearby to supply the lift with electric power. This work is normally carried out by an independent builder and it is, therefore, necessary to ensure close collaboration between the lift manufacturer and the builder, so that the lift is installed as soon as possible after the builder's work is complete. If there is a delay, arrangements must be made to eliminate any danger by temporarily covering the floor aperture or pit.

Figure 91 illustrates the construction of an aperture in a typical domestic upper floor, before the installation of a vertical cabin lift. The approximate size of the opening is 990mm by 1270mm (3ft 2in by 4ft 2in), the floor boards being removed and the joists trimmed, as necessary. A trimmer joist is then inserted at right angles to complete the opening. It is important to ensure that the position and construction of the aperture does not weaken the structure as a whole.

A manually-operated vertical lift can be installed at a lower cost than an electric lift. These lifts, which have counter-balance weights inside the columns, can be operated by a winch of the 'window winder' type. Unless an attendant winch is fitted, the OT must ensure that the disabled person can satisfactorily manipulate the winch to activate the platform. The manufacturers of these lifts undertake the complete installation and builders' work themselves, at an inclusive price.

If a vertical lift is required in an old house of complicated design with more than two storeys, it may not be possible to

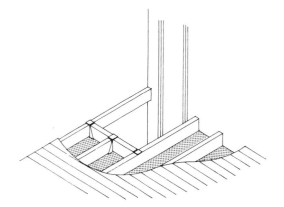

91 Lift-aperture
construction

92 Manually-operated vertical lift suitable for standing or wheelchair use

provide vertical access to all floors via one lift-shaft. This problem can be overcome by incorporating two separate lifts in different positions. However, the OT and disabled person may decide that access to all floors is not essential or that the expense of repositioning the essential amenities could be less than installing a second lift. This would, of course, depend upon the make of lift chosen.

Whilst some form of enclosure or self-sealing trap over the lift aperture is desirable for the reasons stated on p70, the Building Regulations 1976 (England and Wales) provide that, in a two-storey dwelling, a fire-resistant protective enclosure is not mandatory. Instead, a 'modified' half-hour fire-resistance is imposed upon the construction of the upper floor, but no special fire precautions are necessary for the part of the floor in which the lift aperture has been made.

5.3 Stair-lifts

Stair-lifts provide access to the upper floor as an alternative to a vertical-type home lift. Basically, a stair-lift consists of track or rails bolted on to the existing stair treads and a horizontal platform which is winched up and down the tracking, with the aid of a small electric motor and a chain or strong rope. The same safety features and facilities are incorporated as for vertical lifts and preparatory builder's work is normally necessary before installation. Plates 94 and 95 illustrate different designs of stair-lift which can either be fitted with a standing platform or a seat.

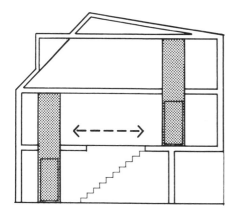

93 Three-storey house served by two lifts

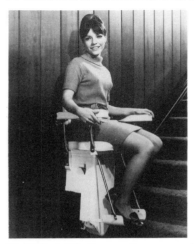 

94, 95 Stair-lifts for standing or seated use

One disadvantage of some stair-lifts is that the effective width of the staircase is reduced by up to one third, which may present a hazard to other members of the household, especially if they are elderly. There must be adequate space at the bottom and, in particular, at the top of the stairs, to park the lift when not in use and for the disabled person to get on or off without danger of falling. Figure 96 illustrates the points to be considered when choosing a stair-lift for a specific dwelling. The lower end of the track should not project into, and obstruct, the passageway. The OT may recommend that extra grab-handles or rails should be fixed in conjunction with the stair-lift.

The most common reason why a particular staircase is unsuitable for a stair-lift is that it changes direction in mid-flight. Unfortunately, the fact that a significant proportion of all domestic staircases contain winders or half landings with a 90° or 180° turn, creates numerous problems when a stair-lift installation is contemplated.

The cornering stair-lift is designed to overcome the problems encountered with awkward staircases. It consists of a seat, travelling on a monorail track which is fitted to one side of the staircase. The chair incorporates a drive unit underneath and both are kept upright, despite any changes in the angle of inclination of the stairs. These stair-lifts are generally more expensive and cannot be used where doorways lead onto half-landings, a feature commonly found in older-style town houses.

Another way of overcoming the problem of half-landings is to use one stair-lift on each flight. This may prove less costly in the long run, depending on the make of lift chosen. However, this arrangement is only satisfactory when the disabled person can walk sufficiently steadily on the half-landing to change from the first lift to the second. Also, an additional handrail would have to be fitted, as shown in figure 2, Chapter 2 p17.

Some stair-lifts are designed to carry a disabled person seated in his wheelchair, but these lifts are much larger and, generally, more expensive, and most of them can only be fitted onto straight flights of stairs. If the disabled person can transfer easily from wheelchair to lift-seat and vice versa, and will be able to continue to make this transfer in the future, economies in cost and space

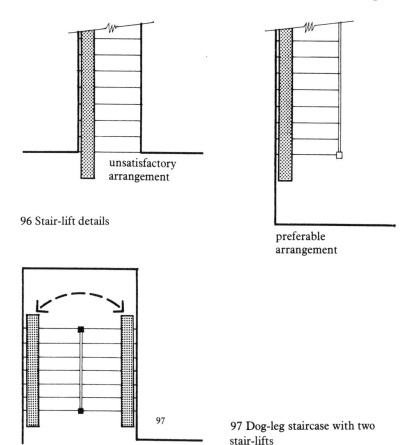

unsatisfactory
arrangement

96 Stair-lift details

preferable
arrangement

97

97 Dog-leg staircase with two
stair-lifts

98 Seated stair-lift capable of negotiating corners

can be made if a smaller lift with an integral seat is installed. Two wheelchairs could then be kept in the house, one on each floor: in appropriate cases, the DHSS will supply the second wheelchair.

It is often assumed that a lift is going to be installed *inside* a disabled person's home but, where objections, obstacles or lack of space make such an installation impossible, the lift may be located outside, with the shaft enclosed in brick or timber. Access to and from the lift-car would be through specially-formed doorways at each level.

5.4 Other considerations

An electric home lift is a relatively expensive piece of equipment, notwithstanding the many benefits it provides. A disabled person may purchase a lift independently and organise the preparatory builder's work himself, but such a lift is normally obtained on permanent loan from the local authority, who may or may not require the occupant to contribute towards the cost of installation. (See also Chapter 1 for details about UK grants.)

Where a lift is required in a local-authority house, permission must be obtained from the relevant housing authority before any work is carried out. When the lift is no longer required, the housing authority will either request its removal and reinstatement of the structure, or allow it to remain if it can be of benefit to a subsequent disabled occupant.

Once a lift is installed, arrangements should be made for regular inspection by the manufacturer or local-authority engineers. Fear of accident occasionally persuades a disabled person to opt for an alternative adaptation. The British Standards, referred to earlier, recommend that users and third parties should be insured or otherwise covered against death or injury arising from the operation of home lifts.

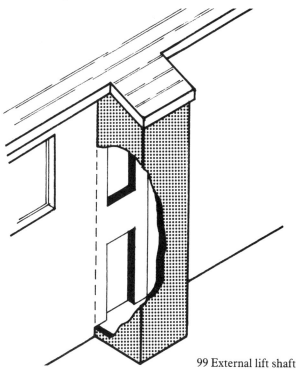

99 External lift shaft

6 Cloakrooms and wcs

6.1 Siting

Disabled people frequently request an additional ground floor wc to be installed. If they need to spend a lot of time in the cloakroom, additional accommodation may be necessary, not because the existing cloakroom is unsuitable or unusable, but simply to free it for use by the rest of the household.

In a bungalow or ground-floor flat, it may be more economical to alter or adapt the existing cloakroom, and provide the new accommodation for the exclusive use of the able-bodied members of the family. Poor access to an existing first-floor wc is a common reason why a second one is needed at ground-floor level. If the disabled person is slow or incontinent, a wc close at hand will prevent much embarrassment and anguish.

The Building Regulations (England and Wales) state that 'no sanitary accommodation shall open directly into (a) a habitable room unless the room is used solely for sleeping or dressing purposes; or (b) a room used for kitchen or scullery purposes'. In most dwellings, the ideal place for a second cloakroom is in an area leading off the main hallway, so that a lobby separating it from the rooms described above is not needed.

If there is adequate headroom, the wasted space underneath a staircase can be used to provide additional sanitary accommodation, but the gas and electricity meters may have to be repositioned. To make the wc easier to approach from the front, particularly for wheelchair users, it can be put against the side wall of the staircase. This will necessitate some building out into the hallway, assuming, of course, that space is available.

Larders of the 'walk-in' type are often located in spaces under stairs, particularly in dwellings built during the inter-war years.

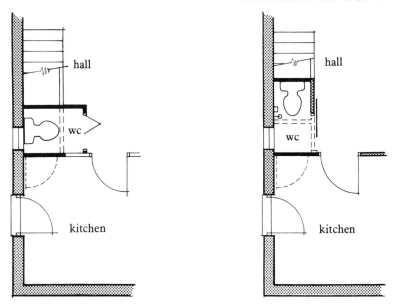

100, 101 Sketch plans of ground-floor cloakrooms located below staircases

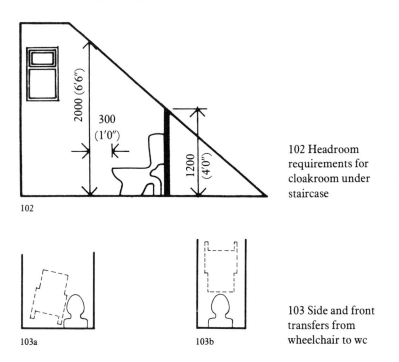

102

102 Headroom requirements for cloakroom under staircase

103a   103b

103 Side and front transfers from wheelchair to wc

In such houses, it may not be possible to create enough space for a second cloakroom, unless the back wall of the larder is demolished and the door repositioned on the hall side.

If there is an adequate window opening, this will provide natural light and ventilation. Alternatively, the most economical solution would be to ventilate the room mechanically with a small electric fan, activated by the light switch.

Where a ground-floor reception room is used as a bedroom, a small cloakroom for the exclusive use of the disabled occupant can be built in one corner. A suitable design has to be agreed, so that the layout of the furniture allows enough space for the wheelchair to be manoeuvred easily inside the room.

An extra wc within the existing structure is, of course, considerably cheaper than building an extension outside, because there will be no need to build foundations, floor, walls and roof. In some circumstances, the siting of an extra cloakroom will be influenced by the proximity of the existing soil drain or the nearest manhole.

Where a shower is required with the new wc, this can be installed in the way outlined in Chapter 4. Although a shower may be desirable, it is not essential, unless the existing bath is unusable or inaccessible. Where a severely disabled person or wheelchair user lives in a two-storey house, a new ground-floor wc is really only a half-measure if access is still necessary to the upstairs bedroom.

6.2 Fittings

A frequent difficulty encountered with the standard wc is that the pan is not high enough. Where the wc is used exclusively by the disabled person, the pan can either be replaced by one with a higher rim level or a proprietary raised seat can be fitted, with 50mm (2in) blocking pieces on the underside. In extreme cases, these two can be used in combination. Where the wc is not for the exclusive use of the disabled person, a raised clip-on plastic seat can be used.

Another problem which calls for close collaboration between the OT and the architect is the transfer from wheelchair to wc. A front approach will require considerably less floor space, but some disabled people can only manage a side approach. This may necessitate structural alterations or the repositioning of adjoining

104

105

106

104 Proprietary seats with blocking pieces underneath

105 Pan with raised rim level

106 Clip-on plastic seat for use when wc not for exclusive use of disabled person

107 Recessed washbasin for use where space is limited

sanitaryware to allow adequate room in which to park the wheel-chair.

For reasons of hygiene, it is always preferable to provide a wash-basin within the cloakroom, and the space available will largely determine the type of basin used. Where space is at a premium, a recessed-type basin, which projects only 150mm (6in) from the wall face, can be built into a wall.

Careful attention should also be given to the type of pillar taps used on wash-basins. People with arthritic hands usually have difficulty in gripping ordinary tap heads, and lever-operated taps may have to be fitted. Lever taps can be fitted in the standard tap positions or used as remote controls at the front of a vanity unit. (See Chapter 2 for kitchen taps.)

The vanity unit illustrated in plate 108 is especially designed for wheelchair users and is supported on adjustable wall brackets, which enable the height to be raised or lowered as desired. Similarly, special wash-basins are available with side control knobs which vary the height: the hot and cold supplies are in flexible piping and the waste pipe is telescopic. It is worth noting, however, that the height adjustment on fittings such as these can only be made by people with fairly strong hands or wrists; however, once the correct height has been determined the fitting will normally remain permanently in that position.

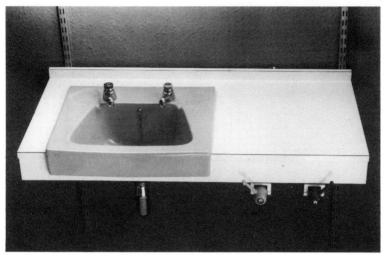

108

109

110

108, 109 Basins of adjustable height with different types of lever tap

110 Clos-o-mat wc providing invaluable aid to personal hygiene

If a disabled person is unable to clean himself after using the wc, the Clos-o-mat Samoa automatic toilet, incorporating warm-water washing and hot-air drying, may provide the only answer. It dispenses with the use of toilet paper and gives complete independence and privacy to severely disabled people. It also serves as an invaluable nursing-aid where patients have to be toileted. The Clos-o-mat can still be used as a conventional wc and can be substituted for the existing pan. The plumbing is connected in the normal way but there must be a 13amp power supply nearby to provide electricity for the small boiler incorporated in the cistern. This is a relatively expensive piece of equipment which needs careful assessment by the OT.

7 Extensions

7.1 Internal requirements

Owing to the high cost of present-day building work, the construction of an extension to provide suitable accommodation for a physically-disabled person is, in many circumstances, viewed as a last resort. Where possible, of course, any necessary alterations are carried out within the structure of the existing dwelling, such as installing a home lift (see Chapter 5) or a wc under the staircase (Chapter 6 p78) so that costs are cut down to a minimum.

Where these internal adaptations are not feasible, a purpose-built extension could provide the ideal solution. Each case must be decided on its merits by the people involved. If a ground-floor extension is not a practical proposition because the site is restricted or awkward, moving to a different house, but not necessarily in a strange area, might be the only satisfactory answer.

Most extensions contain ground-floor bedrooms with or without integral sanitary accommodation, but some provide only a cloakroom. This can be for the exclusive use of the disabled occupant, or for use by the rest of the family (see Chapter 6 p78). The Building Regulations require that any new cloakroom must be separated from a kitchen or reception room by a lobby which, in most cases, can be used to provide, or maintain, existing access to the garden.

The requirements of the disabled person and his family, and the layout of the house, will dictate the particular design. It must not be overlooked that an extension can provide the desired accommodation, but does not facilitate access to other parts of the house: this fact is of particular significance if it is the mother

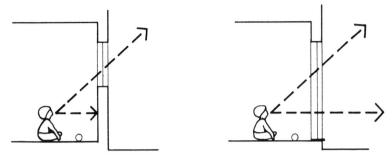

111 Large glazed areas give unobstructed views

who is disabled or wheelchair-bound.

Where a bedroom extension is proposed for a disabled child, he will probably use it as a playroom or bed-sitting-room and, consequently, spend most of his day there. Great care should be taken to ensure that the room is as spacious and pleasant as possible, allowing unobstructed views into the garden so that the child does not suffer from a feeling of isolation or claustrophobia. A large floor area is necessary, so that a wheelchair can be manoeuvred with ease and friends can come in, to enable the child to lead a more normal social life. If he never attains full independence or is mentally, as well as physically, disabled, design features such as internal windows or glazed doors could be incorporated, so that the mother can keep an eye on her child.

Suitable access from the bedroom to the garden must be provided and it is important that the new floor is on the same level as the rest of the home. If it is a husband or wife who is disabled, any bedroom extension should be designed as a double room so that the couple can still be together and the able-bodied partner can provide assistance, if required.

A child with a serious disability can have a feeling of being 'left out' and, if the same child has to sleep in a ground-floor bedroom while the remainder of the family remain upstairs, this feeling can be aggravated. It may also be possible to make a child's bedroom extension large enough for him or her to share with a brother or sister. If this is not practicable, an electrical intercom system could, if necessary, be installed between the rooms.

Not only should the inside of the room be designed with great care but it is just as important that its external appearance should be visually acceptable.

7.2 External appearance

Ideally, an extension should be in scale and harmonise with the design and materials of the existing dwelling. It ought not to be unduly conspicuous and look as though it has been 'tacked on' as an afterthought. Unfortunately, stringent financial constraints encourage such features as flat felt roofs and poor-quality windows, so that money spent on enlarging the home may not enhance the resale value of the property as a whole.

Most planning authorities prefer a large extension to be constructed, with a pitched roof to match that on the existing dwelling. This is usually no problem on single-storey bungalows, but on two-storey houses, a single-storey pitched roof extension abutting the rear wall of the house often collides with first-floor bedroom windows.

To ensure that time and money are not wasted on abortive drawings, the local planning officer should be consulted at the

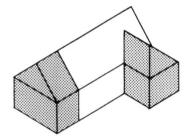 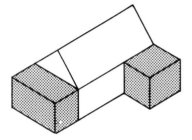

this . . . . is preferable to . . . . this

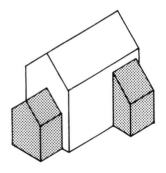 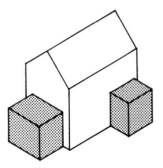

this . . . . is preferable to . . . . this

112 Designs of extensions to single-storey and two-storey houses

113

113 Brick-faced prefabricated extension

114, 115, 116 Selection of single-storey extensions provided by Surrey County Council for disabled people living within the county

114

115

116

outset (see also Chapter 1 p7). Furthermore, it is unwise to assume that, because an extension is intended to meet the needs of a particular disabled person, it will automatically get planning approval.

If extra accommodation is required to provide a new bathroom or larger kitchen in substandard housing (see Chapter 1 p9), a prefabricated unit can be added. This can be erected quickly but Building Regulations approval is still necessary. Prefabricated extensions, obviously, reduce disturbance to the occupants of the house, but some preparatory work, such as site preparation and services, must be carried out before the unit is delivered, and after it has been erected or craned into position. The manufacturers' claims about the economies of these units vary, but the cost of siteworks and sanitary fittings is usually a hidden extra.

7.3 Effect on property value

It is important to consider what effect a purpose-built extension has on the resale value of an owner-occupied house. The cost of most extensions varies between 10 and 40 per cent of the value of the original dwelling to which it is attached, and it is unlikely that this extra investment will be realised if the property is sold, particularly if the locality contains many properties of similar size and design.

A large extension on the rear of a terraced house would not proportionately increase its resale value in comparison with an identical extension on the rear of a one-off detached house. Furthermore, if an extension is tailored too precisely to the needs of the disabled occupant, a future purchaser could be deterred by unusable accommodation.

8 Home dialysis

8.1 Treatment

Renal dialysis or, to be more technically correct, *haemo-dialysis*, is the process of purifying the blood in a person whose own kidneys have failed to function properly. The patient's blood is taken from an artery in his arm and pumped over a plastic membrane in a bath of dialysing solution: the purified blood is then returned into the veins. In the first instance, dialysis is carried out in the hospital renal unit for two or three sessions of four-and-a-half hours each week. This puts a great strain on hospital beds and resources, and may involve the patient in long and expensive journeys.

A dialysis patient is not visibly handicapped in the same way as a paraplegic or arthritic, and the structural adaptations which must be carried out to his home before he can receive home dialysis are very different from those described earlier in the book. Home dialysis installations are carried out by the area health authority: social-service authorities and OTs are not normally involved (see also case study no 2, p110).

During treatment in hospital, patients are trained to administer their own dialysis in the home, usually with the help of a spouse or relative. However, home dialysis should not be regarded as an expedient to save hospital beds. It is the best solution for most patients and enables them to lead as normal a life as possible. Patients treated at home also have a longer life expectancy than those receiving hospital dialysis.

8.2 Accommodation

The first point that must be considered before providing a

home-dialysis room is the availability of essential services. These include an adequate mains water supply, a mains supply of electricity and main drainage. Without these, home dialysis is not a practical proposition and the question immediately becomes one of rehousing.

Assuming, however, that these services exist, the next question is whether there is a room in the house that can be converted, or whether it will be necessary to build an extension or erect a portable cabin in the garden adjacent to the house.

Converting an existing room inside the dwelling is by far the most economical solution. The room needs to be approximately 10 square metres in size and, in order to combat infection, the room must be reserved exclusively for the purpose of home dialysis.

If the house has no bedroom or other room to spare, and bearing in mind that *some* inconvenience is to be expected, a fully fitted-out portable cabin can be installed in the garden. Despite their 'building-site' appearance, these units have the advantage that they are detached from the house and can, therefore, be removed and transported complete, if the patient moves or the unit has to be used elsewhere. Drainage and footings must be installed before the cabin arrives on site, and it is occasionally necessary for expensive lifting techniques to be employed where access to the proposed location in a garden is difficult.

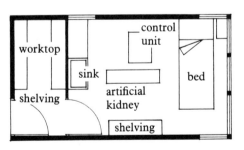

117 Dialysis unit: fitted-out portable cabin

The construction of a purpose-built extension to accommodate a dialysis room is seldom an economic proposition. Whereas the equipment inside the room can be returned to the hospital when it is no longer required, a permanent extension would become redundant, although the room could possibly be put to some alternative use. Where a ground-floor extension is not practical, a loft conversion could solve the problem.

118 Dialysis cabin being lifted into back garden of suburban house

Local-authority approval under the Building Regulations (England and Wales) is necessary for the 'execution of any works and the installation of any fittings', and the conversion of an existing room for home dialysis must comply with the current requirements. The construction of a permanent extension should meet certain visual criteria and planning approval may be necessary, in addition to Building Regulations approval. If there is any doubt, the architect should seek the advice of the local authority at the outset. Local-authority officers are usually quite sympathetic in these circumstances, and approve dialysis schemes submitted to them with surprising alacrity. If the house in which the room conversion is to be carried out is owned by the local authority, the local housing officer must be informed and his permission sought before any work is started. Similarly, in a privately-rented house, a landlord's consent in writing must be obtained, although in both circumstances approval is usually a mere formality, as long as the room is ultimately returned to its original state.

8.3 Equipment

The equipment required in a dialysis room is more or less standard, although different hospital units may require slight variations in specification. Most renal units provide printed hand-outs which set out the general requirements for home installation of dialysis machines, and there must be close collaboration between the architect and the hospital's home dialysis administrator, if a convenient and practicable layout is to be achieved.

When the room conversion is complete, the following equipment is supplied, on permanent loan from the hospital:

  i single bed

  ii dialysis control unit

  iii artificial kidney

  iv water-softener (where necessary).

The area health authority may also help with the cost of a telephone, needed to contact the hospital in case of difficulties.

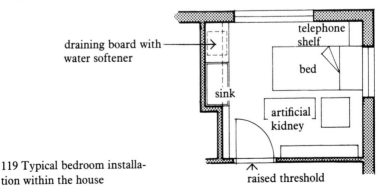

draining board with
water softener

telephone shelf

bed

sink

artificial kidney

119 Typical bedroom installation within the house

raised threshold

The control unit and artificial kidney are located near the bed, because the patient connects himself to the unit by means of injection and plastic tubing. A blood pump is incorporated to assist the circulation through the tubing.

8.4 Services

The services that must be incorporated into, or altered in, the dialysis room are set out below.

Electricity
The existing power and lighting circuits to the dialysis room are disconnected from the rest of the house supply and a new consumer unit incorporated, exclusively serving the dialysis room.

A change-over switch and socket is also installed so that an emergency generator can be connected if there is a power failure.

A cooker control panel is built in near the bed-head to provide a 30amp power supply for the dialysis control unit.

In addition, the following items are necessary:

  i 13amp power sockets for general use

  ii 13amp non-switched socket outlet for water-softener

  iii one or two fluorescent ceiling lights with two-way switches at the door and at the head of the bed

  iv low-wattage bedside light

  v extension socket for telephone placed near to bed-head

  vi battery-operated alarm with bell-push within reach of bed-head and bell placed at the most convenient position elsewhere in the house. (The alarm bell should not be connected to the mains electricity, because any electrical fault would affect the bell itself).

The electricity needed to supply the dialysis room is paid for by the hospital: either a separate meter is installed or the hospital pays a block sum contribution to the quarterly electricity bill. Most hospitals in the UK prefer the latter method, since the former can be open to abuse.

Heating
The temperature within the dialysis room when in use should not fall below 20°C (68°F). Where the house is centrally heated, only a 1kw infra-red wall heater may be needed to boost the room

temperature, if required. In other circumstances, a convector heater or oil-filled radiator may have to be installed to provide background heat.

Water supply
The water supply to the equipment is either taken from the rising main before the rest of the household supply or a new connection is laid from the main in the street, depending upon the requirements of the local water board and/or the condition of the existing supply. It is essential for the architect to consult the local

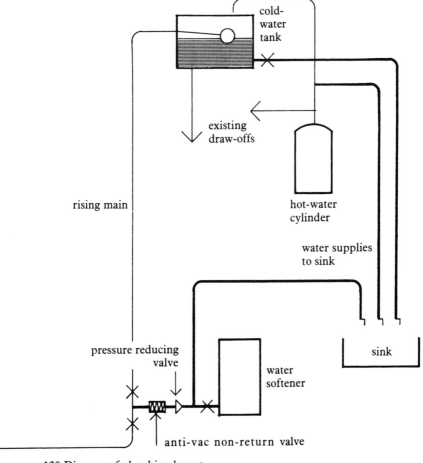

120 Diagram of plumbing layout

water authority at an early stage to get advice on requirements, and obtain a quotation for making a new connection and stop-cock pit. The supply to the water-softener must incorporate an anti-vac and non-return valve, and a pressure-reducing valve if the mains pressure is too high. Flexible connections from the stopcock to the water-softener and the control unit are provided by plastic tubing.

A large sink and draining board will be necessary to wash the artificial kidney boards, and the bib taps should be at least 300mm (1ft 0in) above the rim of the sink. Whatever the size or shape of the artificial kidney, the hospital should advise on the correct cleaning procedure.

Drainage

A 38mm (1½in) trap and waste is run from the sink in the normal way to the nearest gully or soil and vent pipe. Two 19mm (¾in) copper drains are required near the floor, on an outside wall, one to dispose of effluent from the water-softener and the other to dispose of effluent from the control unit. This equipment is connected by plastic tubing to the drains, which may discharge into an outside hopper head or gully grate.

A 38mm (1½in) bath waste and trap is built into the floor, with waste pipe discharging into outside gully or soil-and-vent pipe. This provides an outlet when the floor is mopped down after each session.

8.5 Storage

Sufficient storage accommodation should be provided for eight weeks' medical supplies, although the dialysis room itself may not be large enough to store all of this.

The room should contain:

i 8000mm (26ft 0in) approx of shelving, 300mm (1ft 0in) deep

ii one high-level shelf, 450mm (1ft 6in) deep (possibly over sink) for storage of artificial kidney membranes

iii telephone shelf next to the bed-head.

Wasted areas under the sink and draining board can also be used for storage, if shelves and cupboard fronts are built. Where floor space is at a premium, the water-softener can be placed under the draining board, as long as hinged access is provided.

8.6 Decorations

Bearing in mind the frequent washing-down that is necessary, the finishes must all be washable or waterproof.

The walls should be finished in vinyl wallpaper or paint. The floor should be 'tanked' by laying a pvc sheet covering, with welded and waterproof seams, over a hardboard base.

A coved skirting, 100mm (4in) high, should be provided with welded corners, dressed round all fittings and obstacles in the floor and also carried across the doorway. A raised hardwood threshold across the door opening must, therefore, be built and the door height adjusted accordingly.

9 Glossary of disabilities

Condition	Description	Difficulties
Amputation	The removal, generally by surgical means, of a limb or part of the body.	Person may have to learn how to use an artificial limb. If he is a bi-lateral, lower-limb amputee, he may be wheelchair-bound. May have to learn one-handed activities. Mastectomy may cause difficulties in reaching.
Arthritis	See *Osteo arthritis* and *Rheumatoid arthritis*	
Arterio sclerosis	Narrowing and hardening of the arteries, which can lead to impairment of circulation.	a. Diminution of the blood supply to the brain which can result in poor memory and concentration, and intellectual impairment. b. Diminution of blood supply to extremities, which could lead to gangrene.
Colostomy and Ileostomy	An opening on the front wall of the abdomen bringing the colon or ileum to the surface and thus creating an artificial anus.	This frequently has to be permanent, in which case the person has to learn independent management of own dressings. Person may take much longer than normal in the bathroom.

Condition	Description	Difficulties
Coronary thrombosis	A clot of blood blocks the coronary artery, and the area of heart muscle supplied by that artery is damaged.	Requires a carefully graded programme back to active life. May suffer chest pain and/or breathlessness.
Cerebral palsy or Spastic	Brain injury before or during birth, sometimes bringing about jerky movements. Can affect all or part of the body.	Inability to co-ordinate muscular movement; very often involves musculature of speech, leading to difficulties in communication.
Disseminated sclerosis	See *Multiple sclerosis*	
Friedreich's Ataxia	A hereditary condition which results in jerky incoordination of the lower limbs; the upper limbs are similarly affected later in the disease. There may be mental impairment.	Incoordination of movement, with poor mobility.
Hemiplegia	Paralysis of one side of the body.	Can only use one arm effectively, which may be the non-dominant one. If paralysis on right-hand side, may have speech difficulties. If paralysis on left side, visio-spatial difficulties can occur. May have to use a walking aid.
Incontinence	Inability to control bowel or bladder, or both.	May have to wear protective pads, clothing or appliance. May not be able to manage these independently. Susceptible to urinary infections.

Condition	Description	Difficulties
Incontinence *continued*		Will need extra time in bathroom, particularly if incontinent of bowel.
Muscular dystrophy	Results in progressive weakness and flaccidity of the muscles.	May have to be confined to a wheelchair. Progressive difficulties in walking, sitting and respiration.
Multiple sclerosis (also known as Disseminated sclerosis)	Results in a mixture of symptoms including muscular weakness and incoordination. Can have intention tremor (a tremor which occurs when a specific movement is attempted). Eyesight may be affected. There may be mental impairment.	May have incordination of hand or eye, and unsteady gait. Eventually could be wheelchair- or bed-bound. At a certain stage, the person may become incontinent.
Osteo-arthritis	Stiffness, pain and often swelling in the weight-bearing joints (ie hips and knees). Loss of hip and knee movement.	Stiffness on bending, sitting, kneeling and walking. May not be able to reach a low oven or own feet. Often needs a walking aid and may not be able to carry things. Difficulties with toileting, and ascending stairs.
Parkinson's Disease (Paralysis agitans)	Brings rigidity and poverty of movement. Tremor particularly noticeable in the fingers, hands and upper limbs. Face becomes mask-like in appearance. May have shuffling gait and impaired speech.	Difficulties in fine finger co-ordination, writing, handling cutlery, etc. May have problems getting up from chair or managing stairs. Speech may become inaudible.

Condition	Description	Difficulties
Paget's Disease	Inflammation of one or more bones, causing a thickening of the bone. May become deaf and fractures occur easily, particularly in the femur.	Stiffness and pain on moving affected limb. May be unable to bend at hip or knee.
Paralysis	Loss of muscular control.	Will be unable to move or control affected part of the body.
Paraplegia and Quadraplegia	Paraplegia involves total or partial paralysis of lower limbs. Quadraplegia (tetraplegia) involves total or partial paralysis of upper and lower limbs.	Mobility in wheelchairs. Voluntary movements of limbs and sensation affected. Bowel and bladder control may be impaired. May need extra time in lavatory, so that additional facilities are needed for rest of family.
Poliomyelitis	Complete or partial paralysis of muscles.	May have problems in any motor activity – walking, bending, carrying, holding, reaching, breathing, etc. Could be wheelchair-bound or may have to use a respirator.
Renal failure	Kidneys cease to function, and are unable to excrete body's waste products.	Fluid is retained in the body and swelling occurs. Brings with it lassitude, depression and a rise in blood pressure. Home dialysis unit may be required.
Rheumatoid Arthritis	Pain and swelling of small joints, bringing bony changes, wasting of muscles and eventual deformity.	Pain and discomfort in most movements. Inability to get up off low chairs or manage stairs is common. Bending, reaching and stretching

Condition	Description	Difficulties
Rheumatoid Arthritis *continued*		can be a problem and often the grip is very weak. Person may have bad days when little is possible.
Slipped Disc	Disc of cartilage, situated between the vertebrae, may protrude and press on, or irritate, nerve root as it leaves the spinal cord.	Causes pain and limitation of movement at site of the protrusion. Difficulties with bending, stretching and lifting are common.
Spina Bifida	A congenital deformity of the lower parts of the spine, often associated with hydrocephalus.	Brings paralysis of lower limbs and loss of control of bowel and can mean difficulties in maintaining the sitting position.
Stroke	A vascular catastrophe in the brain which brings about hemiplegia.	See *Hemiplegia*
Spastic	A general term applied to people suffering from Cerebral paralysis.	See *Cerebral palsy*
Thalidomide	Often gross congenital deformities, sometimes involving failure of limb function and/ or internal abnormalities.	May be wheelchair-bound, unable to use upper or lower limbs. Sight, hearing, speech may be involved. Difficulties in walking, feeding, dressing. Often requires individually adapted equipment.

Appendix A
Case studies of adaptations

This appendix contains four detailed case studies, intended to highlight the nature of possible adaptations, together with the practical and emotional problems which may be encountered in their implementation. From these examples, it can be seen that structural alterations can provide improved independence and mobility for the disabled person, although the building work involved is often fraught with practical problems and bureaucratic delay. Nevertheless, in most cases, the initial disturbance and anxiety is outweighed by the long-term benefits to the disabled person and his family.

Case study 1: Independence for a young Londoner

This case study concerns the two-floor extension and adaptation of a four-bedroomed detached house, in an Inner London borough, for a severely physically-disabled man. This involved the addition of a downstairs utility room and upstairs purpose-built bathroom, to house a vertical lift-shaft for an electric wheel-chair lift, and the provision of an overhead tracking hoist to run from bath to bed.

On 25 March 1972, Mr N, then 32 and a carpenter by trade, fell 3600mm (12ft) while at work on a building site and suffered an incomplete C6 lesion. He was transferred to the National Spinal Injuries Unit at Stoke Mandeville, where he remained, apart from occasional weekend visits home, until July 1973. At the time of his accident, Mr N lived with his wife and three children, two boys, aged seven and five, and a baby daughter of a few weeks, in a small house which had been converted into two self-contained flats, both owned and occupied by the family. Mrs N is a qualified nurse but was not working, due to the recent birth of her daughter. The marriage was happy and stable.

The accident, which could not have happened at a worse time for Mrs N, obviously strained and depressed her to a great extent. She was reported to be 'very much at sea' and 'on the verge of tears' for several months but, by August 1972, was again coping well at home, deriving great comfort from her baby daughter, looking forward to her husband's return and better able to accept the frustrations of the waiting game for allowances and adaptations to the home. The two flats were already proving too small for the whole family and were considered unsuitable for any major conversion. Minor adaptations, such as ramps and wider doors, were recommended by the National Spinal Injuries Unit but took many months to approve and implement. In fact, these delays put back the date of Mr N's discharge from Stoke Mandeville. By then, he had, however, learned to feed and wash himself with the use of aids, but needed some help with dressing and the attachment of his urinal, and complete assistance with all transfers to and from his wheelchair.

It was clear by September 1973, two months after his return home, that the family had already come across many major practical and emotional problems with regard to Mr N's readjustment to his wife, children, friends and neighbours. Many of these were resolved by discussion. Mr N felt extremely caged in and frustrated by his own limitations and the smallness of the flats.

He became a television addict and found it difficult to balance his own complete dependence on his wife with the equally pressing demands on her of his young daughter. This conflict was compounded by the daughter's initial inability to relate to Mr N as a father, although the two boys were very pleased to have him home. Mrs N became increasingly stressed by the tremendous demands on her as a mother, wife and nurse, and the relationship with her husband became very strained. Holiday arrangements for Mr N, through the Winged Fellowship Trust, which have now become annual, helped to ease the situation.

Mr N's brain and senses had in no way been affected by his accident and he began, with the full support of his Department of Social Services – mainly his occupational therapist – to seek ways of becoming even more independent and mobile. However, all efforts to obtain part-time work for him, to retrain him for employment and to teach him to drive again proved unsuccessful. Mr N, therefore, concentrated his attentions on his home environment and, when the opportunity arose, contemplated the purchase of a larger house in the same neighbourhood, using the compensation monies he had received.

Before doing so, however, he discussed the implications of this with his local authority's senior building surveyor and occupational therapist. He learned that planning permission for any extensions to the intended new house would be possible,

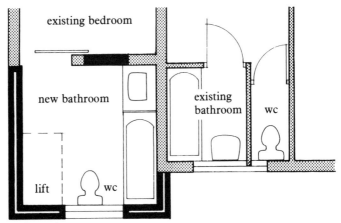

121a First-floor plan

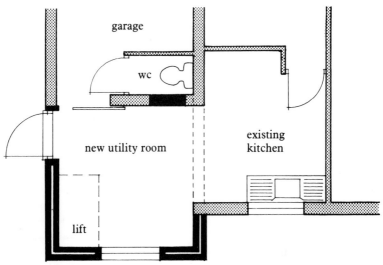

121b Ground-floor plan

although there was no gurantee that the council would be able to make any contribution towards these. Mr N decided to go ahead and purchased the larger house, the irony of the situation being that, but for his own financial resources, the council would have been obliged to rehouse Mr N and his family, anyway, the flats having proved patently unsuitable.

At the beginning of July 1974, the local authority's Director of Social Services wrote to the Director of Development, requesting a feasibility study 'to build on to the back of the house a unit to take a lift and a special bath unit; with overhead tracking hoist to run from bath to bed'. Plans were drawn up and the approval of the District Surveyor obtained. Tenders were invited in October and an estimate for £7,247 accepted in November, although this was finally reduced to £6,978. An additional £1,789 was estimated for the purchase and installation of a Home Elevator wheelchair lift and an electric hoist. The Director of Social Services was notified of the accepted estimates on 20 November and asked to give the necessary financial authority to proceed. Since nothing had been heard by January 1975, a further letter was sent by the Director of Development, pointing out strongly that the contractor was unlikely to hold the price much longer and that Mr N could not move in until the works were completed, nor sell his present house until he had vacated it. Mr N's patience had also become exhausted and he had, meanwhile, written to his MP, seeking help. Authority was forthcoming within a fortnight and work started in mid-February.

The financial arrangements were as follows:

Purchase of house	£21,000
Adaptations	£6,978
Lift and hoist	£1,789
	£29,767
Council grant (aids to daily living)	£1,789
Mr N (from his compensation monies)	£27,978
	£29,767

Consideration of financial support for Mr N was being made at the same time as the Housing Act 1974 was becoming law, and the provisions of this Act were not, therefore, taken into accountnt.the local authority felt that, because of the high rateable value of the new house and the assumed intentions behind Mr N's compensation, the full costs of the purchase of the house and the expensive adaptations to it should be met by Mr N. It did, however, agree to plan and supervise the works, to order and purchase the lift and hoist, and to pay for those items of equipment as aids to daily living. Mr N was consulted about the financial arrangements and the intended plans, and the advice of the Department of Social Services and the National Spinal Injuries Unit was sought on the proposed adaptations and aids.

Nevertheless, there was some breakdown in communications as, in December 1974, the local-authority occupational therapist wrote to Mr N saying that she had just seen the plans and felt the conversion could have been done more economically, so that the rateable value of the house would be kept as it was instead of being increased. It was, however, too late to makeee any changes. Mr N himself considered there had been a lack of liaison and ideas between Stoke Mandeville and the Department of Social Services. He also objected mildly to being asked to pay the full cost price for the adaptations to the local authority before work had even commenced.

Initially, the builders made good progress and, by early May, completion was expected on 1 June. Unfortunately, there were problems. Despite the fact that the order for the lift was placed in October 1974, delivery was delayed and not anticipated until July 1975. Unsuccessful efforts were made to accelerate this, as Mr N could not move in until it had been installed. There had, in fact, been some design difficulties all along: first, the manufacturers had expressed reservations about the safety aspects of the planned trap and, later, the District Surveyor had requested stronger bolts to fix the tracking to the external wall. Even as late as May, modifications were being made – the builder being told that floor traps would be required and the manufacturer being asked to fit heaps to the lift platform. The first completion date was not met and a new date at the end of June was agreed. Mr N, naturally, expressed considerable concern at this further delay and, to speed matters, agreed to find another decorator for the works, at his own expense, provided this amount was deducted from the original contract price. This was agreed. He also thought that the builders and the lift manufacturers were not working properly together. In June, Mr N complicated matters by requesting other alterations to the house, which were not relevant to the initial adaptations. A quotation of £669 was accepted for these – the full cost to be met by Mr N – and the original builders started work on these aspects as well. Installation of the lift took place in July, and Mr N and his family moved in during the same month.

The fact that Mr N had, himself, worked in the building trade could not have made life easy for the contractor and, since he was living on site, he offered a great deal of advice. Mr N believes that his advice was valuable and ensured a higher standard of work. Certainly, some suggestions made by Mr N in respect of a false floor in his bedroom, to make this level with that in the extension's bathroom, and in respect of the tracking for the hoist, were very sensible. The builder was, however, somewhat upset. The hoist and its ancillary equipment was installed during July and August, but without the type of sling Mr N wanted. He therefore returned the provided hammock type and purchased the one he wanted privately. The builders reported that they had completed their work by the middle of August but Mr N disputed this and claimed that various things remained to be completed. The disagreements continued for seven months and were only resolved in April 1976 after legal action had been threatened by Mr N. The whole saga had lasted nearly two years.

There is no doubt that the adaptations carried out by the local authority have now proved very satisfactory. Mr N's independence has been considerably increased: he is able to move throughout the house and have his own private area at the same time. The family, too, are living a fuller life. Mr N studied for, and recently sat, a GCE A-level examination. Mrs N is contemplating returning to work part-time, knowing that her husband can be left happily on his own at home. The provision by the local authority of many additional aids, including an electric wheelchair, a remote-control intercom/door-lock system, and a special telephone, have helped considerably, as had a typewriter donated by the Spastics Society. In addition, the local and health authorities arranged for a district nurse to visit Mr N for two hours every morning and for an ex-fireman to call once a week to give Mr N a bath. These arrangements, coupled with the lift and hoist, have relieved Mrs N of many of the duties she was undertaking initially and have eased the strains on all concerned.

Case study 2: Home treatment for kidney patient

This case study concerns the ground-floor extension to a modern semi-detached, two-storey house, situated in a rural borough council area, to accommodate a home dialysis unit. The house contains three bedrooms and is occupied by a family of five, consisting of the father, a lorry driver with previous lengthy service in the army; the mother, a canteen assistant; and three children, two boys and a girl, now aged fifteen, twelve and ten, respectively. The dialysis unit was for the younger boy, Vincent, who had suffered from kidney trouble since birth. Treatment of this condition had been by antibiotics but, just before Easter 1977, Vincent collapsed at school with complete renal failure and was admitted to a large hospital in a city approximately sixty miles away. The parents were then told that his only hope of survival lay in regular treatment on a kidney machine, three times a week, until such time as a transplant operation could be performed. Dialysis could take place either at that hospital or at home, if the necessary adaptations and arrangements for this could be made.

A successful application was made to the Department of Health and Social Security to cover the costs of the regular 120-mile round trips to the hospital, and transport was provided on a rota basis by neighbours, friends and volunteer drivers from local organisations. However, it quickly became clear that these arrangements could not continue indefinitely as, not only was Vincent's education being totally disrupted, but happy family life was also being seriously disturbed. The mother's earnings were dramatically reduced, in spite of the generosity and understanding of her employers. The father, too, had occasionally to take time off work. Meal-times became irregular. The dependency on friends and neighbours became daily more embarrassing and could not be relied on in the long term. Family stresses increased. It also became clear that facilities for dialysis could not be provided indefinitely by the district hospital, as its limited resources were already stretched. The lengthy journeys were proving extremely tiring for Vincent and his family. There was a danger of hepatitis from infected blood. A home dialysis unit became essential.

For home dialysis, a room reserved exclusively for this purpose is required, because the risk of infection is high. The original idea was to house the unit in an existing bedroom, but the loss of a bedroom with a mixed family was not practicable and could not be seriously considered. The second idea was to provide a cabin in the back garden but this was unsuitable as it would isolate Vincent from the rest of the family. The simple solution was to build a single-storey extension measuring 3750mm by 2300mm (12ft 6in by 7ft 6in) on the gable wall of the house, with internal access from the hallway through a sliding door. A timber lean-to conservatory had first to be demolished and foundations laid. The extension would then be constructed of cavity brick-work with a solid floor and a flat well-insulated three-layer felt roof. The approved plan included two large windows to provide adequate light and ventilation; a bin store with a lockable door at the rear of the extension for the disposal of dialysis waste; a gully waste from the angle wash-basin and a floor drain connected via a new manhole in the rear garden to the main sewerage system; a quarry-tiled floor with coved skirtings to allow effective cleansing; decoration; and shelving and storage units. The electrical system was a complicated specialist affair, as an electrical change-over had to be provided, for generator use in the event of a power failure. Heating was by means of a 3kw electric fan heater.

The adaptation of the family house was, therefore, no problem, nor was the provision of the home dialysis equipment, as the area health authority for the hospital where Vincent was receiving treatment accepted responsibility for this. The obstacles were largely financial. The borough council felt strongly that all costs should be met by the National Health Service and not from rates but, nevertheless, speedily processed an application on behalf of the family and, during the early summer of 1977, agreed to pay half the cost of the required dialysis room by means of an Improvement Grant under the provisions of the Housing Act 1974. There was considerable local publicity in the press about Vincent's position. Thought was given to the family, itself, financing the balance required, which it could have done, but this possibility was rejected by the local authority on moral grounds. Local voluntary organisations raised monies to assist but the father refused to accept charity and passed all donations on to the local hospital. The area health authority, in whose area the family lived, adamantly refused to assist. The remaining alternative was the other area health authority, which had agreed

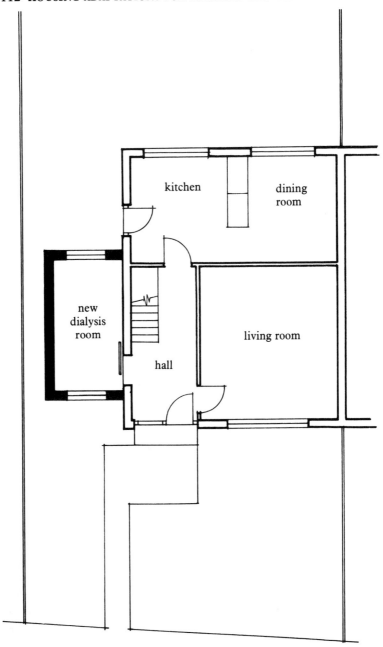

122 Plan of single-storey extension to accommodate dialysis unit

to provide the dialysis equipment. However, there were many difficulties – such a financial contribution would have been contrary to agreed policy and the house to be adapted was situated in another regional health authority's area.

The uncertainty about the funding of the balance of the costs lasted nine months but approval was, eventually, given by this area health authority, when it was pointed out that Vincent's trips to the hospital were costing £40,000 per annum, whereas home dialysis would cost only £400 a year, a considerable saving to the National Health Service. The authority now began to move more quickly, and appointed an architect to plan and supervise the adaptation. This architect lived in the distant city and had to make several visits to the borough council to see the family house and discuss technical and financial matters, naturally at a cost to the employing authority. A few design problems were ironed out on site and, in fact, the final proposals for the extension came from the architect. Tenders were sought by the area health authority and, eventually, an estimate of £2,677 was accepted. The financial breakdown of this was as follows:

Total cost of works	£2,677.00
(tender date, November 1977)	
Borough council	
Improvement Grant (Housing Act 1974)	£1,338.50
Area health authority	
Grant (Health Services and Public	
Health Act 1968)	£1,338.50
Total grant	£2,677.00

The only difficulty was that the builder selected by the area health authority, a man well-known to them, was based nearly forty miles from the house to be adapted. Builders based within the borough council area, close to the house, had been rejected when tenders were considered. Delays in construction resulted because of the distances to be travelled daily by personnel and materials. Building work thus started in January 1978 and was completed in early April. The dialysis unit was installed immediately, the mother having previously been trained in how to operate it. The whole exercise had therefore taken just over a year – nine months being devoted to obtaining decisions and three months for actual construction work. Support from local voluntary organisations continued to the end, with the presentation to Vincent of a deep comfortable armchair, instead of a bed, and a portable television set for his dialysis room.

Vincent is now able to join in fully once again with the rough-and-tumble of a normal schoolboy existence and can carry out dialysis outside school hours in the comfort of his own home. Family life is also much happier. The adaptation itself has proved successful and home dialysis effective, in spite of some initial medical reactions from Vincent. The family awaits only news of the promised kidney transplant operation.

Case study 3: Time runs out for disabled couple

This case study concerns the adaptation of a kitchen in a small semi-detached house in a London borough for a woman suffering from multiple sclerosis.

In 1972, Mrs B, who was married with two children – a son about to go to university and a daughter of fifteen in her O-level year – was diagnosed as having multiple sclerosis and, by February of that year, her deterioration had reached the point where an electric wheelchair was prescribed for her. Her husband, an engineer, had had a serious accident at work. Thus, instead of holding down a good job as a consulting engineer, he had become substantially handicapped, although still ambulant, as a result of his injuries. In consequence, he became rather irritable for much of the time, and was forced to earn an inadequate living teaching engineering students at home. On legal advice, he brought an action against the company whose negligence led to his injuries and, although the facts were not contested, the firm's insurers decided, predictably, to defend the action. While both the plaintiff and the defendant's solicitors knew that settlement would be reached eventually, and that damages were likely to amount to tens of thousands of pounds without the matter getting to court, they also knew that the date of settlement would be delayed for as long as possible. No damages were, therefore, likely to be forthcoming for two or three years.

The family live in a modest, two-storey, semi-detached house in one of the London boroughs. In this respect, they are fortunate, as the London boroughs combine both housing and social-services functions. In another respect, however, they are unfortunate, as the rateable values in their area are high. Irrespective of their need, because the rateable value of their house is £15 over the statutory limit of £450, they are not entitled to more than minimal grant aid to help adapt the house.

When the Bs first approached the local authority for help in 1977, they were visited, on different days of the same week, by a social worker, an occupational therapist and a surveyor, and an administrative officer from the environmental health department. Within three months, Mrs B had been advised that:

1 because of the high rateable value of the family house the Bs were not eligible for more than the minimum statutory grant. In their case, this would apply in relation to the provision of three new kitchen fittings in the breakfast room of the house, as Mrs B was clearly having difficulty in getting down the existing step into the present kitchen. It was also pointed out that the authority was generously prepared to meet the cost of making the necessary manhole connection required if the newly installed kitchen was to function satisfactorily

2 it might be possible at some time in the future for a loan to be made available to the family to carry out further alterations. The loan would be secured against a legal charge on the property, and the work funded by this means would be suject to detailed scrutiny by the authority

3 in the opinion of the authority, the family would be more suitably housed in a bungalow in Peacehaven, if they could purchase one, despite the fact their son was taking his A levels, and the daughter was approaching her O levels

4 where any proposals for adaptations were concerned, it was assumed that Mrs B's disability was stable and that her husband's was irrelevant.

Within six months of being notified of this, Mrs B found herself confined, for most of the day, to her newly-prescribed electric wheelchair. She now had to be lifted bodily down three steps by ambulance attendants whenever she left the house for her once-weekly outings to her local disability club/clinic at the hospital where she was receiving treatment, and at which she usually met her social worker. Her social worker, although also an occupational therapist, had no domiciliary experience.

Mrs B was eventually told that the borough architect's department had decided what her requirements were in her kitchen. They had produced a drawing and brief specification and, having three tenders, had instructed a contractor to proceed with the necessary work without any further reference whatsoever to Mrs B. Being an enterprising person, Mrs B contacted the Disabled Living Foundation. The DLF put her in touch with some specialist architects who, having visited her family, produced a scheme to suit her requirements within a fortnight. They suggested their proposals should form the basis for discussions in relation to the provision of an interest-free loan. They were ignored, and Mrs B was advised that she should be most cautious about encouraging 'her architects' to behave in so precipitate a manner. For instance, 'it should be made quite clear that if there was any additional cost involved in specifying a sink unit suitable to take waste disposal unit, even if this were to be provided by the client, any such cost must be borne by the clients themselves'. The authority's social work administrator said that a 100mm outlet on the sink 'could cost £100'.

After daily telephone calls and many letters, the authority eventually reluctantly agreed to consider the architects' proposals in committee. The discussions lasted for over an hour and the scheme was referred back for 'reconsideration'. The architects were not allowed to be present, and the dialogue which followed had to be conducted by letter. The scheme was referred back three times more and, eventually, after a further eight months including the summer-holiday break, the scheme was approved in its original form.

It was unfortunate that a revised price then had to be negotiated with the contractors whose original tender had been successful, and this, in turn, was the subject of committee approval. At last, all was ready for work to start, and the family braced itself for the arrival of the builders on site. By this time, Stephen had been at university for nearly a year. Gloria was only a year short of taking her A levels. Mr B had still not recovered any damages, and was becoming more and more lame. Two days before the builders arrived, Mrs B died.

Case study 4: Country cottage modernised for elderly man

This case study concerns the provision of essential bathroom and kitchen facilities in a fairly isolated country cottage, owned and occupied by a wheelchair-bound man.

The cottage was first visited, and the problem assessed, in

October 1975. The sole occupier was a man of 64 who had been virtually confined to a wheelchair for twelve years. He suffered from arthritis in the hip and spine, and his right leg had been amputated below the knee, following a fall in his home. Although the cottage had two first-floor bedrooms and two further attic rooms, the ground-floor rooms only were in regular use. There were no bathroom facilities and the toilet was a simple Elsan, situated directly off the rear hall. This arrangement was, obviously, totally unsuitable. The rear kitchen area had been partitioned to form a gloomy hallway, kitchen and poorly-ventilated store. The kitchen roof sloped steeply to an internal ceiling height of 1,575mm (5ft 3in) at the eaves. The overall internal ceiling height was a maximum of 1,800mm (6ft 0in). This, together with insufficient natural light and ventilation, meant that the house was very dark.

It was obvious from the start that the man did not want to move to specialised accommodation and that the two ground-floor rooms were the only area of the house easily accessible to him. The living room could also be used as a bedroom and, as the man lived alone, this created no problems.

The unsatisfactory existing rear extension was demolished to ground level and the new kitchen/bathroom extension built off the existing foundations, in concrete blocks rendered to match the existing building. The steep sloping roof was replaced by a flat felt roof. The bathroom and kitchen were then designed, taking into account the recommendations of the occupational therapist. The roof joists were made sufficiently strong to enable a ceiling track and electrical hoist to be fitted, to allow transfer from the toilet or wheelchair to the shower in the bathroom, and the hand-shower set installed enabled the man to have a shower while seated on the bench in the shower area. The wc was set at the correct level to allow easy transfer from the wheelchair, and the wash-basin and sink set at a correct height to allow access for a wheelchair user. The floor level was made constant throughout the ground floor, and a concrete ramp built to give access to the kitchen from the rear garden. An electric immersion heater provided hot water. A 100mm (4in) drain was laid to a newly-constructed septic tank in the garden.

The works, commenced in January 1977 – about fourteen months after the initial enquiry, were finally completed in August 1977.

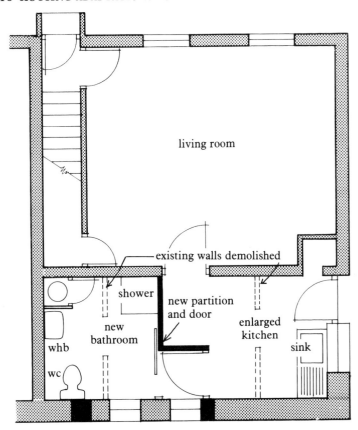

123 Plan of internal alterations

The reasons for the fourteen-month delay in starting work were entirely financial. The occupier had no capital, and his sole income was from Supplementary Benefit. An Improvement Grant under the provisions of the Housing Act 1974 was, of course, available and the (then) maximum grant of £1,600 was approved on 22 November 1976. The total cost of the work was £3,950.94. In December 1976, the County Council Social Services Department offered a grant of £600 plus the loan of the electric hoist. The remaining amount could not be raised by the occupier. A maturity loan under section 37 of the Local Government Act 1974 was arranged by the council in whose area the man resided.

The loan was fixed at a maximum of £3,000 and approval of

that amount was obtained on 29 November 1976.

Under a maturity loan, the capital sum is not repaid, only the interest. As the occupier was on Supplementary Benefit, the Department of Health and Social Security agreed to pay the interest element of the loan. The borough council will not recover the capital sum until the house is sold and, as the value of the house is far in excess of the loan amount, the council's loan is secure.

The financial breakdown was as follows:

Council	
Improvement grant	£1,600.00
Maturity loan	£3,000.00 (max)
County Council	
Social Services Department	
Grant under the provisions of the Chronically Sick and Disabled Persons Act 1970	
(plus loan of electrical hoist)	£600.00
Total amount available	£5,200.00

Work started in January 1976, when the financial problems had been satisfactorily resolved. By April 1976, the work was virtually completed but a series of visits by council personnel during the next four months was necessary to ensure the satisfactory completion of the tracking and hoist system, because of electrical problems.

In December 1977, a further Improvement Grant of £371.00 was approved by the council to assist with the re-roofing of the cottage and a waterproofing treatment to the cottage walls. The total cost of this work was £742.00 and the grant represented half of the cost. The remaining 50 per cent of the cost was added to the existing maturity loan. By April 1978, the work was completed.

This case clearly demonstrates that it *is* possible to overcome all technical and financial problems, even if it takes an extremely long time because many different disciplines are involved. This one case involved a builder, plumber, electrician, building control officer, solicitor, accountant, housing manager, occupational therapist, social worker, home help and environmental health officer, as well as medical personnel.

Appendix B
Addresses of UK organisations concerned with disablement

All the addresses and telephone numbers given below were correct at time of going to press (March 1981); in case of doubt readers are advised to consult the Disabled Living Foundation, 01–602–2491.

Age Concern
Bernard Sunley House
60 Pitcairn Road
Mitcham, Surrey CR4 3LL
01–640–5431

Arthritis Care (British
Rheumatism & Arthritis
Association)
6 Grosvenor Crescent
London SW1X 7ER
01–235–0902

Association for Spina Bifida
& Hydrocephalus
Tavistock House North
Tavistock Square
London WC1H 9HT
01–388–1382

British Epilepsy Association
Crowthorne House
New Wokingham Road
Wokingham
Berkshire RG11 3AY
034–46–3122

British Polio Fellowship
Bell Close
West End Road
Ruislip, Middlesex HA4 6LP
71–75515

Centre on Environment for the
Handicapped
126 Albert Street
London NW1 7NF
01–267–6111

Chest, Heart & Stroke
Association
Tavistock House North
Tavistock Square
London WC1H 9TE
01–387–3012

College of Occupational
Therapists
20 Rede Place
London W2 4TU
01–229–9738

Disabled Living Foundation
346 Kensington High Street
London W14 8NS
01–602–2491

Greater London Association
for the Disabled
1 Thorpe Close
London W10 5XL
01–960–5799

Help the Aged
32 Dover Street
London W1 2AP
01–499–0972

Invalid Children's Aid
Association
126 Buckingham Palace Road
London SW1W 9SB
01–730–9891

Joseph Rowntree Memorial
Trust
Family Fund
PO Box 50
Shipton Road
York YO3 6RB
0904–21115

Kings Fund Centre
126 Albert Street
London NW1 7NF
01–267–6111

Multiple Sclerosis Society
286 Munster Road
London SW6 6AP
01–381–4022

Muscular Dystrophy Group of
Great Britain
Nattrass House
35 Macaulay Road
London SW4 0QP
01–720–8055

National Children's Bureau
8 Wakley Street
London EC1V 7QE
01–278–9441

National Society for Autistic
Children
1A Golders Green Road
London NW11 8EA
01–458–4375

Parkinson's Disease Society of
the United Kingdom
81 Queens Road
London SW19
01–946–2500

Royal Association for
Disability & Rehabilitation
25 Mortimer Street
London W1N 8AB
01–637–5400

Spastics Society
12 Park Crescent
London W1N 4EQ
01–636–5020

Spinal Injuries Association
5 Crowndale Road
London NW1 1TV
01–388–6840

Voluntary Council for
Handicapped Children
8 Wakley Street
London EC1V 7QE
01–278–9441

Appendix C
List of Manufacturers contributing material

Manufacturer	*Page*
Amilake Ltd	19, 67
Armitage Shanks Sales Ltd	56
Banbury Buildings Ltd	88
Barking Grohe	34
Chiltern Medical Developments Ltd	57
Clos-o-mat (GB) Ltd	84
Conseal Ltd	64
Expamet Industrial Products Ltd	39
Heatrae Sadia Heating Ltd	61
Homecraft Supplies Ltd	52, 54, 81
Longwell Green Reinforced Plastics Ltd	40
Mecanaids Ltd	53
Medic-Bath Ltd	55
Minivator Sales Ltd	74
Nicholls & Clarke Ltd	32, 35, 52, 65, 81, 83
Geo. Moore & Co Ltd	30, 33
Nottingham Handcraft Ltd	41
Portakabin Ltd	93
H. C. Slingsby Ltd	40
Stairlift Engineering Ltd	74, 76
Surgical Medical Laboratory Manufacturing Ltd	28
Terry Personal Lifts	43, 72
Twyfords Ltd	82
Vessa Ltd	45
Walker Crosweller & Co Ltd	61

Appendix D
Addresses of information sources

This book includes references to a wide range of aids and equipment and it is, therefore, unrealistic to attempt to include all the addresses of suppliers or manufacturers concerned.

The following list gives addresses of centres from which information concerning aids and equipment may be obtained:

British Isles

Disabled Living Foundation, 346 Kensington High Street, London W14 8NS.
01–602–2491
Publishes regularly updated information sheets concerning aids and equipment (including details of suppliers) and runs a telephone/letter enquiry service.

Scottish Information Service for the Disabled, Claremont House, 18/19 Claremont Crescent, Edinburgh EH7 4QD.
031–556–3882
Publishes regularly updated information sheets concerning aids and equipment (including details of suppliers) and runs a telephone/letter enquiry service.

Information Service for Disabled People (Northern Ireland), 2 Annadale Avenue, Belfast BT7 3JH.
Belfast 640011
Can provide information sheets concerning aids and equipment (including details of suppliers) and runs a telephone/letter enquiry service.

Information Service for the Disabled (Republic of Ireland), 29
Eaton Square, Monkstown, Co. Dublin.
Dublin 809251
Runs a telephone/letter enquiry service and can give information
about suppliers of aids and equipment.

Exhibitions of aids (Aids Centres)
The Aids Centres listed below are exhibitions where a selection
of aids for disabled people can be seen and tried out. They have
been set up to provide information to those professionally concerned with disability, and to disabled people and their friends
and relatives.
*Visitors should always contact the Centre before visiting, as an
appointment is usually necessary.* As the Centres vary considerably
in size, content and the kind of services they offer, it is also wise
to check that the purpose of the visit can be fulfilled.

Birmingham	Disabled Living Centre, 84 Suffolk Street, Birmingham B1 1TA 021–643–0980
Caerphilly	Aids and Information Centre, Wales Council for the Disabled, Llys Ifor, Crescent Road, Caerphilly CF8 1XL. 0222–869224
Edinburgh	South Lothian Aids Distribution and Exhibition Centre, Astley Ainslie Hospital, Edinburgh EH9 2HL. 031–447–9200
Glasgow	Aids Advice and Resource Centre, The Florence Street Clinic, 26 Florence Street, Glasgow G5 0YX. 041–429–2878
Leicester	Medical Aids Department, British Red Cross Society, 76 Clarendon Park Road, Leicester LE2 3AD. 0533–700747

Liverpool	Merseyside Aids Centre, Youens Way, East Prescott Road, Liverpool 14. 051–228–9221
London	Disabled Living Foundation, Aids Centre, 346 Kensington High Street, London W14 8NS. 01–602–2491
Newcastle-upon-Tyne	Newcastle-upon-Tyne Council for the Disabled, Aids Centre, MEA House, Ellison Place, Newcastle-upon-Tyne NE1 8XS. 0632 23617
Southampton	Hampshire Area Health Authority, Southampton General Hospital, Shirley, Southampton SO9 4XY. 0703–777222 ext: 3122 or 3414
Sheffield	Sheffield Aids Centre, Family and Community Services, 87/89 The Wicker, Sheffield 3. 0742–734839
Stockport	Aids/Assessment Unit, Stockport Area Health Authority, Stepping Hill Hospital, Stockport. 061–483–1010 ext: 207
Wakefield (a small standing exhibition of aids with special exhibitions at regular intervals and an information service)	National Demonstration Centre, Pinderfields Hospital, Pinderfields, Wakefield 0924–75217 ext: 2510 or 2263

Overseas

The following organisations are able to supply details of aids and equipment available, together with manufacturers'/suppliers' names and addresses, and information about the availability of services for disabled people in each country.

Australia
Australian Council for Rehabilitation of the Disabled, Acton House, Edinburgh Avenue, Canbera City, ACT 2601.
Independent Living Centre, PO Box 212, Carlton South, Victoria 3053.
Independent Living Centre, St. Margaret's, 411 Payneham Road, Felixstow, S.A. 5070.
Independent Living Centre, 60 Havelock Street, West Perth 6005.
Independent Living Centre, PO Box 351, Ryde, N.S.W. 2112.

Austria
Allgemeine Unfallverischerungsanstalt, Adalbert Stifterstrasse 65, 1200 Vienna XX.

Belgium
Belgian Red Cross Society (Croix Rouge), 98 Chausée de Vleurgat, 1050 Brussels.
Fonds National de Reclassement Social des Handicapés, Rue du Meiboom 14, 1000 Brussels.

Canada
Canadian Rehabilitation Council for the Disabled, Suite 2110, One Yonge Street, Toronto, Ontario M5E 1E8.

Denmark
Dansk Hjaelpemiddelinstitut, Gregersensvej 1A, DK-2630 Tastrup, Denmark.
Socialstyrelsen (National Board of Social Welfare), Kristineberg 6, Postbox nr 25 55, 2100 Copenhagen Ø.

France
Comité National Francais de Liaison pour la Réadaptation des Handicapés, 38 Boulevard Raspail, 75007, Paris.

Germany (Federal Republic)
Rehabilitation International Information Service, c/o Stiftung Rehabilitation, 6900 Heidelberg 1, PO Box 101 409.

Hong Kong
Rehabaid Centre, Hong Kong Society for Rehabilitation, Room 802, Duke of Windsor Building, 15 Hennessy Road, Hong Kong.

New Zealand
New Zealand Crippled Children Society, PO Box 6349, Te Aro, Wellington.
Aids and Information Centre for the Handicapped, c/o Building Centre, 211 Cashel Street, Christchurch 4.

Norway
Norwegian Committee of Rehabilitation International, Radet for Funksjonshemmede, Rom 616 Sporveigst 10, Oslo 3.

Sweden
Swedish Committee of Rehabilitation International, Handikap-pinstitutet, Fack, 161 25, Bromma.

Switzerland
Pro Infirmis, Postfach 129, 8032 Zurich.

United States of America
National Rehabilitation Information Centre, 8th and Varnum Streets, Catholic University of America, Washington DC 20064.

Accent on Information, Gillum Road and High Drive, PO Box 700, Bloomington, Illinois 61701.

Bibliography

1 Standards and guides

British Standards Institution. *Code of practice for access for the disabled to buildings* BS 5810: 1979. London, BSI, 1979.

British Standards Institution *Code of practice for design of housing for the convenience of disabled people* BS 5619: 1978. London, BSI, 1978.

British Standards Institution *Specification for mobile, manually operated patient-lifting devices* BS 5827: 1979. London, BSI, 1979.

British Standards Institution *Specification for powered homelifts* BS 5900: 1980. London, BSI, 1980.

British Standards Institution *Specification for powered stairlifts* BS 5776: 1979. London, BSI, 1979.

Cheshire County Council, Department of Architecture. *Made to measure* (3rd ed) Chester, CCC, 1980.

Darnbrough, A. and Kinrade, D. *Directory for the disabled* 2nd ed. Cambridge, Woodhead-Faulkner, 1979.

Department of Health and Social Security *Instantaneous electric water heaters for shower purposes: suitability for use by disabled people* London, DHSS, 1980.
Available on request from DHSS Health Publications Unit, Archives Registry, Scholfield Mill, Brunswick Street, Nelson, Lancashire BBN 0HU.

Disability Alliance *Disability rights handbook for 1980* London, Disability Alliance, 1980.

Elliott, P. *The garden and the handicapped child* London, Disabled Living Foundation, 1978.

Essex County Council *Design Guide for residential areas* Chelmsford, ECC, 1973.

Foott, S. *Handicapped at home* London, Design Council, 1977.

Foott, S. ed. *Kitchen sense for disabled people of all ages* London, Heinemann, 1975.

Goldsmith, S. *Designing for the disabled* 3rd ed. London, RIBA Publications, 1976.

National Building Agency *The disabled in rehabilitated housing: guidance for housing associations* London, NBA, 1978.

Penton, J. *Handbook of housing for disabled people* Hayes, London Housing Consortium West Group, 1976.

Rudinger, E. ed. *Coping with disablement* 2nd ed. London, Consumers' Association, 1976.

Tarling, C. *Hoists and their use* London, Heinemann, 1980.

Walter, F. *Four architectural movement studies for the wheelchair and ambulant disabled* London, Disabled Living Foundation, 1971.

Walter, F. *An introduction to domestic design for the disabled* London, Disabled Living Activities Group, Central Council for the Disabled (now Disabled Living Foundation), 1968.

White, A. S. et al. *The easy path to gardening* London, Reader's Digest Association, 1972.

2 Legislation and circulars

Chronically Sick and Disabled Persons Act 1970. London, HMSO, 1970

Highways Act 1980. London, HMSO, 1980.

Housing Act 1974. London, HMSO, 1974.

Rating (Disabled Persons) Act 1978. London, HMSO, 1978.

Department of the Environment *The Building Regulations* 1976. London, DOE, 1976.

Department of Transport *The Use of Invalid Carriages on Highways Regulations* SI 1970 1391. London, HMSO, 1970.

Department of the Environment *Adaptations of housing for people who are physically handicapped* Circular 59/78. London, HMSO, 1978.

Department of the Environment and Welsh Office *Housing Act 1974 – improvement of older housing* DOE Circular 160/74. London, DOE, 1974.

Department of the Environment and Welsh Office *Housing for people who are physically handicapped* DOE Circular 74/74. London, DOE, 1974.